PENN FAMILY RECIPES

COOKING RECIPES
OF
Wm. Penn's Wife, GULIELMA

Edited by

Evelyn Abraham Benson

---

with

AN ACCOUNT OF THE LIFE OF

GULIELMA MARIA SPRINGETT PENN,

1644–1694

by Evelyn Abraham Benson

GEORGE SHUMWAY, Publisher

York, Pennsylvania

1966

GEORGE SHUMWAY, *Publisher*

R.D. 7, York, Penna. 17402

TO THE HISTORICAL SOCIETY OF PENNSYLVANIA

IN APPRECIATION

OF

THE LOVING CARE

WITH WHICH THE SOCIETY

HAS COLLECTED AND PRESERVED

PAPERS OF THE PENN FAMILY

FOR WELL OVER A HUNDRED YEARS

Acknowledgments

Grateful acknowledgment for courteous and untiring assistance is made to J. Harcourt Givens, Manuscript Curator at the Historical Society of Pennsylvania, to Conrad Wilson, formerly Assistant Librarian at the Historical Society of Pennsylvania, to Miss Dorothy Lapp of the Chester County Historical Society Library and to Miss Ellen Shaffer, Rare Books Librarian, Philadelphia Free Library. Excerpts from William Penn's letter of 6 August 1684 are published by permission of the Pierpont Morgan Library, New York.

The Editor

Evelyn Abraham Benson has read an incredible number of original Pennsylvania colonial documents in a lifetime as a free lance researcher. Every manuscript holds for her more excitement than a mystery story; she delights in discovery and identification of obscure but significant documents, incidents or individuals associated with Pennsylvania's earliest days.

This interest was sparked by bedtime stories about the Indian wars which her father had heard from his mother on the southwestern Pennsylvania farm where the family lived for generations. In the large semi-rural family connection of her childhood she observed the arrogant independence of the Ulster Scot fused with the gentleness, integrity and loyalty which these people carried as a heritage from the peaceful sects, Quaker, Brethren, Mennonite, who were their forebears.

A curiosity about Pennsylvania people and their origins led her to a permanent involvement with Pennsylvania colonial documents. Wellesley College and Columbia University supplied her with a training in scholarship permeated by a passion for accuracy.

Contents

This picture, painted on glass, was believed to be a portrait of Gulielma Maria Springett Penn when Maria Webb wrote *The Penns and Penningtons* early in the nineteenth century, and it is so titled in her book. *Courtesy Historical Society of Pennsylvania.*

Introduction

Gulielma

Gulielma Maria Springett, first wife of William Penn, is one of the neglected heroines of American history. Although she never left England, she contributed substantially to the founding of Pennsylvania—materially, with her estate, and spiritually with her undeviating sympathy and support for her husband's noble aim to establish a government in which tolerance and freedom of conscience should be basic principles. She was the inspiration of William Penn's finest thoughts, the companion of his best days.

Strangely enough, the many letters which she and Penn wrote to each other have almost completely disappeared. The few surviving letters, and accounts of Gulielma by her contemporaries, reveal a person of rare gifts, mentally, spiritually and physically. These gifts she devoted wholly to support and strengthen the body and soul of the unusual man who was the Founder of Pennsylvania.

It is fitting that a book of recipes, both for food and for healing medicines, should be the largest existing document of Gulielma Maria Penn, for she spent her loving life in nourishing a large household and in administering to the ills of family, friends and neighbors.

Identification of the manuscript

The collection of cooking recipes presented here is the second part of a previously unidentified and unpublished four-part, 158 page, manuscript book of recipes and cures in the Penn Manuscript Collection of the Historical Society of Pennsylvania, Philadelphia. The cooking recipes occupy 61 pages, numbered 1 through 57, two pages being blank where the transcriber accidently turned two leaves at once, and two pages being unnumbered. At the beginning of the series of recipes is written, "My Mother's Recaipts for Cookerys Presarving and Chyrurgery—William Penn." At the bottom of the last page of the recipes is written, "Here ends the book of Coockary in great hast transcrided by Edward Blackfan the 25th of October 1702."

What was going on in the Penn household at Worminghurst, Sussex, in October 1702 that would require great haste in the transcribing of a cook book? Apparently the answer is that William Penn, Jr. planned to sail for Pennsylvania within the next two weeks and would take the comfort of his mother's cookery abroad with him, for in 1702 (the month is blurred but seems to be October 28) William Penn wrote to James Logan, "my son . . . thinks of sayling in 10 or 12 days."

Ever since William Penn's return to England from Pennsylvania the year before (1701), he had been mentioning in letters the imminent departure of his son, William, Jr., for Philadelphia. One delay after another presented itself, the departure finally taking place toward the end of 1703, which gave Edward Blackfan another year in which to transcribe two more sections of recipes, but these were for cures and medications, not cookery. Perhaps the original recipe book belonged to William Penn Jr.'s sister Laetitia, or for some other reason had to be left behind.

William Penn, Jr., arrived in Pennsylvania toward the end of December 1703, or early in January 1704. He remained less than a year. It is possible that when he returned home precipitously the recipe book remained behind at Pennsbury, eventually being sent to England with the Penn Papers assembled by the sons of Hanna, second wife of William Penn, the Founder. In the nineteenth century this manuscript in several unidentified sections came into the possession of the Historical Society of Pennsylvania along with many other Penn papers.

There can be little doubt in attributing the recipes, both for cooking and for medications and cures, to Gulielma Penn. The heading, "My Mother's Recaipts for Cookerys Presarving and Chrurgery—William Penn," and the signature of Edward Blackfan with the date 1702 immediately narrows the field to the mothers of William Penn, Senior and Junior. Internal evidence in the manuscript points to Gulielma. Recipe #97, "To make an oring Puding sister Louthers way," refers to Margaret Lowther, sister of William Penn, the Founder, hence the recipes must have belonged to the wife of William Penn, the Founder. The attribution is fortified by the fact that the collection of cooking recipes is associated with a large number of medicinal recipes, including 29 pages of eye remedies. Guli's grandmother, Katherine Partridge Springett, had been famous throughout England for doctoring abilities and especially for her skill with eye ailments. Guli also was noted for her ability and skill at curing, and it may be assumed that knowledge of these matters together with the written recipes and medications came to Guli through her mother and grandmother.

Guli Penn died in 1694, aged fifty years, and the manuscript was transcribed eight years later, in 1702. The recipes, both for cooking and curing, should be associated with a mid-seventeenth century date rather than with the relatively late transcription date.

Arrangement of the manuscript

When Edward Blackfan was asked to copy the recipes of William Penn, Jr.'s mother, there was at Worminghurst a copybook with many blank pages in it. In the front were twenty-nine written pages, chiefly cures for the eyes, but the blank pages were ample for transcription of Gulielma's cookery and cures. The leaves of the copybook evidently were loose when it was purchased by the Historical Society of Pennsylvania, and when these pages were attached to the pages of a large volume labeled *Miscellaneous Mss. William Penn 1674–1716 VI*, a few pages were not placed in their correct original order.

Part one of the manuscript comprises 29 pages, written in an unidentified hand, more clear, precise and scholarly than that of Edward Blackfan whose handwriting fills all the remaining pages. This section, with its emphasis on medicine for the eyes, surely is an inheritance from Guli Springett's grandmother, Katherine Partridge Springett, who was famous for eye cures.

Part two is the book of cookery herein printed, and previously described. Page 1 of the cookery section is the verso of the last page of *part one*. It is mounted on page 81 of the Penn manuscript volume, as is page 2 with one blank side. Page 3 of the cookery section, with one blank side, is mounted on page 55 of the manuscript volume. The pages of the cookery section numbered 4 through 57 are arranged consecutively on pages 55 through 79 of the manuscript volume.

Part three consists of 51 manuscript pages headed "Recaipts of Physick and things and waters out of my mothers Book." At the end is written, "Here ends the Book of Physick as transcribed by Edw. Blackfan."

Part four consists of 16 pages headed, "Recaipts of oyntments and such Like of my Mothers."

The three parts of the manuscript involving ointments, medications, and cures are published separately, as a companion volume to this cook book, under the title *PENN FAMILY MEDICATIONS.*

Edward Blackfan, the transcriber

Edward Blackfan was born 16 February 1653, a son of John Blackfan of Steyning, Sussex. His father was a convinced Friend who was prosecuted as a Quaker in 1659, 1662, and 1663. Edward himself was indicted for absence from national worship in 1681 and imprisoned with eight other Quakers in Horsham Goal.

He seems to have made a voyage to Pennsylvania in 1686, for several letters of that year addressed to friends in Philadelphia by William Penn refer to Edward Blackfan as the bearer. In his own letter of 6 September 1689 Edward Blackfan says, "I question whether I may see Pensilvania aney more," the last two words implying that he had seen Pennsylvania previously.

Edward Blackfan married William Penn's cousin, Rebecca Crispin on 24 October 1688. William and Gulielma Penn, with their children Laetitia and Springett, signed the marriage certificate.

At the time of the wedding the Penns and a number of others were ready to sail for Pennsylvania, expecting to embark before the year was out. But less than a month after the Blackfan wedding William of Orange landed in England and James II, Penn's friend, fled to France. England was in turmoil. William Penn's position, as a friend of the old regime, became precarious.[1]

A year later, in September 1689, Edward Blackfan, with a commission from William Penn to collect revenues in the province and to be steward of all Penn's plantation, was aboard ship with his wife and all their goods, riding at anchor in the Downs, ready to sail for Pennsylvania, when an embargo put a temporary end to all shipping, and a permanent end to Edward Blackfan's Pennsylvania venture.[2]

Family tradition gives 1690 or 1699 as the date of Edward Blackfan's death, and states that his wife Rebecca came to Pennsylvania with the Penns in 1699,[3] but Penn documents

4

establish that Rebecca Blackfan was at Worminghurst, Sussex, in 1700, present at the birth of a child to William Penn, Jr. In the series of recipes transcribed in 1702 the handwriting and signatures of Edward Blackfan are identical to the handwriting and signature of his original letter to Phineas Pemberton, 6 September 1689, in the collections of the Historical Society of Pennsylvania. This establishes that Edward Blackfan was alive in 1702. Hanna Penn's letter of 27 December 1703 to William Penn mentions Edward Blackfan, apparently a member of the household at Worminghurst. Her letter of 12 May 1713 to James Logan implies that Rebecca Blackfan is en route to Pennsylvania and states that "her poor husband [Edward Blackfan] is dead and I would not have her want." Upon the arrival of Rebecca Blackfan and her son William in Pennsylvania in 1713, they became caretakers of Pennsbury where, we are justified in presuming, Gulielma Penn's Book of Cookery was a part of the household equipment.[4]

References

1. Blackfan Notes, Albert Cook Myers Collection, Chester County Historical Society.
2. Edward Blackfan to Phineas Pemberton, 6 Sept. 1689, Etting Papers, Pemberton I, 33, Historical Society of Pennsylvania.
3. Blackfan, Elizabeth C. (1909) The Blackfans of England and America: *Papers Read Before the Bucks County Historical Society*, II, p. 102–105.

   Blackfan, Elizabeth C. (1929) The Blackfans of England and America: *Pennsylvania Magazine of History and Biography*, 53, p. 193.

   Blackfan of Steyning, Sussex: Albert R. Justice Collection, Genealogical Society of Pennsylvania.
4. Drinker, Sophie Hutchinson (1958) *Hannah Penn and the Proprietorship of Pennsylvania:* Philadelphia, p. 22, 46.

Transcription and editing of the recipe manuscript

Although the recipe manuscript that Blackfan transcribed is written in English, it is by no means a simple matter to read it or to re-transcribe it. Edward Blackfan wrote a seventeenth century script in which a number of letters were made in a manner considerably different from what is common practice today. Additionally, the manuscript contains a number of words now obsolete, and has many other words of quaint spelling. The combination of these factors makes some pages of the manuscript almost unintelligible to an inexperienced reader, and by no means are they immediately clear even for one with considerable experience in reading old documents.

The recipes printed here have been transcribed for printing as faithfully as possible, preserving the original spelling and word order. The meanings of obsolete words are given in footnotes, to assist the twentieth century reader. In the course of the transcribing it was noted that the recipes became more intelligible and readable if arranged somewhat like blank verse rather than in the run-on paragraphs found in the manuscript, hence the small liberty was taken to present them in the more readable form; word order remains unchanged.

The only other liberty taken with the original manuscript has been to rearrange the order of the recipes so that they are grouped into a few obvious categories, such as meat, fish & fowl, beverages, baked goods, etc. The arrangement of the recipes in the manuscript is almost random. A consecutive series of numbers was assigned to the recipes as they are arranged in the manuscript, and these numbers are found immediately following the title of each printed recipe. If for any reason it is desired to re-establish the original order, it can be done by arranging the numbered recipes consecutively.

Reproductions of a few sample recipes from the original manuscript are given here, in the Appendix, including the important first and last pages that date and identify the manuscript.

MY MOTHER'S RECAIPTS FOR COOKERYS

PRESARVING AND CHYRURGERY

WILLIAM PENN [Jr.]

[**MEAT**]

[**FISH**]

[**FOWL**]

Too Make Hagasyes [Haggis]

[4]

Take a Calves gin or Chaldarn,
Ripe it and scoure it well with salt,
then par boyle it,
chop it
put there too one pound of sewett,
and all the marrow of a marow bone,
then grate the Crums of a peneworth of white bred,
put them to it
putt there to 2 pounds of Curants
1/2 a pound of sugger, or more,
sum nutmeg and Cinomon
quantity of peper,
and a qr. of a pound of dates,
a qr. of a pint of Rose water,
12 eggs

a Litell quantaty of Creme,
mingle them altogether—

Haggis, *a popular English dish until the 18th century, but now considered especially Scotch. A dish consisting of the heart, lungs, liver of a sheep or a calf, etc. mixed with suet and oatmeal, seasoned with salt, pepper, onions, etc. and boiled like a large sausage in the maw of the animal.*
Chaldarn, *chaldern, chaldron, chawdron, entrails of a beast, especially as used for food.*

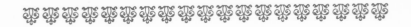

Too Make Shreed Pyes

[6]

Take a Legg of good Larg muton
Cut it in shreds and par boyle it,
then dry it in a Cloath, and shred it very small
and 3 pound of beefe sewett very small,
3 pound of Currants bubeled in a Cloath
and not mashed
a qr of a pound of suger or more,
3 nutmegs beten,
a Litell salt —
12 spunfuls of Caraway seed, beaten
the peels of an oring shred small,
1/2 a dusen of pippins pered, and shred small,
2 or 3 spunfuls of Rose water,
12 dats slised,
a Litell mase Cinomon slised,
a good Legg of muten with this will make 15 pyes —

Rose water, *the water from boiled rose petals, a popular addition to countless recipes for centuries, even to the present time. A recipe of 1430 directs: "Take Quynces, caste them on a potte, & caste there-to water of Rosys."*
Pippin, *the name of numerous varieties of apples raised from the seed.*

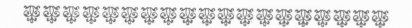

Too Stew a Rump of Beefe

[7]

Take a very good Rump of beefe and pouder it 3
or 4 days
then 1/2 boyle it,
then take a Litell fresh beefe,
a Litell parsly,
a Litell spinaige,
a Litell sweet margerum,
a few oinyons
a prity dele of beefe seuit, mix all these together,
then seson it with a Litell peper and nutmeg,
then take up youre beefe stuf
saving all the gravey that Come out of it,
then put it into a pot
with 2 or 3 handfulls of Liquor it was boyled in,
put a Litell mase in it
so Lett it stew softly, till it bee enough,
then take it up with all the gravey,
put a Litell venigar in it,
and a Litell sweet buter,
and serve it upon sipets—

Pouder, powder, *to season or preserve food with salt or spice.*
Sipet, sippet (*supett in Wycliff*), *a diminutive of sop; a small piece
of toasted or fried bread, usually served in soup or broth, or with
meat, etc., or used for dipping into gravy.*

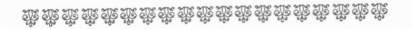

A Curious sauce for a Leg of Mutton Boyled

[8]

Take the bottam of 2 or 3 hartz chocks, being
tender boyled,
and as much meat as you siruped from the Leves,
then take a Littell of the muten broath,
a pece of sweet butter,
a few scalded gousberyes,
green grapes or barbarys,
a Litell veniger and suger,
so sarve it upon sipetts —

Hart, *a male red deer with antlers, a stag.*
Chock *or chuck, in the midland counties of England means the 3
ribs of beef nearest to the neck, cut straight down the forequarter to
about half way through the shoulder blade.*
Siruped, *syruped, with this meaning, and used as a verb, is not found
in the Oxford Dictionary of English, nor any other dictionary of
unusual words consulted.*

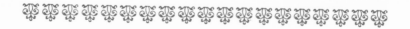

Too Rost a Leg of Mutten

[9]

Take Cloves and stick it,
then shred a good Dele of beefe suett very small
season the suet with a good Dele of grose peper,
and a prety dele of salt,
so stuff the Legg of mutten with it in many places,
as you doe beefe with parsly and rost it
this pleses many tasts very well—

Too Boyle muton Chines

[23]

Take youre mutton, put it into the watter
with Long mase, parsly winter savory:
tyed in a buntch
the botams of white Loves [loaves],
and when it is well boyled take it up,
and put a great peece of butter into it,
and beat it together,
and sarve it up with Sippetts
put Capers in to it—

Chine, *spine or backbone. It is used of a saddle of mutton and of any part of the back of beef, ribs or sirloin.*

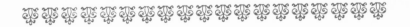

Too Pickell oystors:

[27]

Take a bushall of shelld oystors and wash them
Clene in the water thay Came from,
then sett faire water one the fire till it begin to seithe
then put in youre oystors
and 3/4 of a pint of white salt
so Lett them boyle simering skiming it,
when thay bee boyled take them of,
and Lay them one by one on a cloath, and
Dry them well
then take the clere of the juce of the oystors —
and strain it and sett it one the fire
with 1/2 an oz of Cutt ginger,
and 1/2 an oz of grose peper
a 1/3 of an oz of Long mace
so Lett it boyle, and bee scumed,
when you take it of strain it
and pick out all the mace
and stand a day,
then Lay the oysters a bout with the mace,
sum here and ther
a Cloufe and a bay lefe betweene,
second, now then pore the Liquor one them
and keep them Cloas,
and put halfe a pint of white wine in the Liquor.

Too Stew Oystors

[33]

Take a quart of oysters,
and put them into a skilett with ther Liquor,
and sett them one the fire to boyle
puting in to them a hole oynion,
a blade or 2 of mace
sum hole peper,
so Lett them boyle,
then take them up and Drain the Liquor from them,
then put to them almost a pint of white wine,
and when thay have stewd a while in the wine
putt into them fouer Anchovis,
and so stew them untill the Liquor bee thick,
then Rubb the botam of the dish with
1/2 a pound of butter,
then pore the oysters into the Dish,
sturing them a bout till the butter bee melted —
then Ring into them the juce of a Lemon
so send them up with sipets of frentch breed —

So Season a Patridg Pye
[38]

Take peper
salt
nutmegs
mace
and a Littell suger,
and Rubb the belyes of the partridgs there with
put a hole yonyon in the pye—
put not much butter in it
but when it is baked and Cold
fill it to the top of the pye—

Too fry oystors Mrs. Burns
[40]

Take youre oysters
and wett them in the yeolks of eggs
and buter youre frying pann very well
and fry them as quick as you Cann—

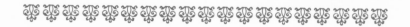

Too Make a Beefe Puding

[49]

Take a pound of beefe and
1/2 pound of beefe sewet
and shred it small,
season it with peper, salt nutmegs and sweet herbs,
worke it up with sum yeolks of eggs,
boyle it in a Collwort levfe
and when it is boyled
put in sum buter and eat it—

Colewort, *originally a general name for any plant of the cabbage kind.*

Too Bake a shoulder of mutton for Venison

[50]

Take youre shoulder too beat it while it bee black
while it is warme together saufe the blood
and when the muten is sufficently bred [brayed,
beaten]
Cutt it of and Dipe it in the blood 2 or 3 times.
then Cutt it and seson it,
and bake it in a pasty with Clarett wine—

To Make a Coller of Beefe

[56]

Take the thinest end of a Cost [side] of beefe
bone it and Lay in pompe [pump] water, and a
Littell salt 3 days
shifting it onece every day,
and the Last Day put a pint of Clarett Wine into it,
and when you take it out of the water
Lett it Lye 2 or 3 houers a Draining
then Cutt it allmost too the end in slices,
then bruse a Littell Cuckanete [coconut]
and a very Littell Allum,
and mingle it in Clarett wine and
culler the meat all over in it
then take a Dusen of Anchovis,
wash them and bone them,
with Cloves, mase peper and 2 hanfuls of salt
a Littell sweet mariarum, and time —
when you make them up Roule the Inmost slise first
and the other 2 tow gether upon it
being very well seconed [seasoned] every where,
and bind it up hard with tape,
then put it into a ston pott sumwhat grater
then the Coller,
and pore on it a pint of Claret wine,
and 1/2 a pint of vine viniger,
a sprigg of Rosmary and a few bay Leaves,
and bake it very well,
before it is quite Cold, take it out of the pot,
keep it dry as Long as you plese —

Too Boyle a Carpe

[58]

Take a Live malle Carpe,
rub him very well with salt, while hee is a Livfe
then wash him very well,
then Cutt him in the neck —
but not so Deepe as too the gall,
Lett him bleed in a Dish too a Litell white wine —
sturing of it as it Drops, Cutt open the Back
and strew upon him a Litell shred ginger
and 1/2 a nutmeg shred, and sum salt
put a pint of white wine and an oynion
a bundle of herbs, as mariarum, winter savory
Cover it, and Lett it boyle,
then turn it as much one the other side,
then take 8 Anchovis, and
put it in sum of the Liquor too Desolve,
then put a quartor of a pound of sweet buter
and Lett it desollve, then pore the blood in it,
then take out youre fish when thay are boyled,
put it into the Dish then putt these Anchovis
and the buter when melted —
and the blood in to the kitell to that
that it was boyled in
and Lett it bee butt through warme
then put it all into the Dish,
put it with almons Rung a mongst them,
you must boyle youre eye and youre Carpe heed first
it must boyle before the Rest,
you must Rubb youre Dish with garlick —

Too Stew Eals as at the sunn in fish Street London

[57]

Take the eals Cutt them in peces,
and put to them so much wine as will Cover them,
a qrtr of a pint of vineger,
oinyons parsly and sorill Choped together
Anchovis 3 or 4 According to the dish—
large mace, a Rase of ginger
a clove or too—

Too Bake eals

[59]

Cut eles from the bone
wash them Clene
take wardens
core and mince them small with the eals,
seson them with Cloves and mace and sanders
put dates pinens and great Resons
put them into the Coffin
so bake them—

Wardens, *large baking pears.*
Sanders, *sandalwood.*
Pinens, *piones (?) the seeds of the peony which were formerly used as a spice.*
Coffin, *in cookery the crust of a pie, a pie dish or mould. Found as early as 1420.*

Too Stew Larks

[60]

Take Larks and Draw them,
and Cut of there feet,
then take quantaty of marrow
and Lett them stew to gether on a Chafing dish,
then take Corants and putt in to the broath
and a few Croms of manchets,
stew them together and Lay them on tostes —

Draw, *there are 6 pages on the word* draw *in the New English Dictionary (Oxford) but I believe #50 is the meaning used here, i.e. "To draw out the viscera or intestines of; to disembowel (a fowl, etc. before cooking, a traitor or other criminal after hanging)." Example cited: "1655: Take a Goose or Duck that is fat, pluck it and draw it." The* **manchet** *so often mentioned in these recipes referred (c. 1420– c. 1791) to the finest kind of wheaten bread, eaten by the upper class. We would call it a roll. A 1688 quotation: "A Rowle, a Manchet, a Wigg, is white Bread, moulded long ways, and thick in the middle." In 1655 another kind of bread was described as "of middle size between Gentleman's Rolls or little Manchets, and the great Loaves used in yeomans' (farmers') Houses."*

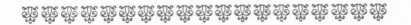

Too make a puding of pigs Liver

[61]

Take a pigs Liver
slompe it with a spunfull of Creme,
strain the whits and yeoliks of 2 eggs,
put them into a qr of a manchet, finly grated
2 or 3 spunfulls of Creme,
Cloves
mace
a Littell suger
a good quantaty of beefe suet Cutt small —

Slompe *did not appear in any dictionary consulted, but every reader will instantly know the meaning.*

Too Make a Puding in Mutten

[62]

Take grated breed,
yeolks of eggs Rosted hard and slised very fine,
corants
parsly
time
Rosmary
shreed youre herbs very fine
put a Litell suger
Cloves
mase
put all these together
between the skin and the flesh of the mutton
and so Rost it with the meat—

Too make puding after the Allmon fashon

[65]

Take a pece of Lene muton
mince it small
then the marow of 3 or 4 bons
Cut the marow in small peces Like past,
take salt and the yeolks of ggs and mix it together,
then take a Clene earthen pot,
fill it halfe full of the broath of beef or mutten
that is fresh and sett it one the fire,
then make balls of the minse meat
and put them in one after an other in the broath,
Lett them boyle softly
then take them up and put to them white wine,
buter and suger—

Allmon fashon. *Donald Kent of the Pennsylvania Historical and Museum Commission suggests that this comes from the French,* **à l'Alle- mand,** *i.e. in the German fashion.*

Too Make a Biske

[88]

Take of beefe mutton and vele,
boyle them together in water 5 or 6 houers,
then take out the meat and put into the broath
a hen or tow,
and Lett them boyle an houre or more,
then take them out and put then into som broath
pidgins and
yong Chickens 1/2 a scoure [score] or Less
according to youre broath
put in sweet bred and Cox Combs,
Lambs stons
Rasher of backen,
the Carnalls of sheeps heads
Lett these boyle an houer at the Lest, then
putt in the gravey of too or 3 Leggs of mutton at Lest
season it with salt,
sarve it up — with the meat in it —

Biske, *a rich soup made by boiling down birds, etc.*

24

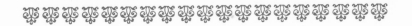

Too make Pigg Brann [Brawn]

[105]

Take a Large sow pigg, very well fed
of 6 weeks old or upwards,
when it is scalded and Drest
Cutt of the heed Close too the shoulders
Cut of the feet as you use to doe when you Rost one
then Cutt down Clen throu the Chine in the back
then bone it,
Leving as Littell flesh as you Can on the bons,
Lay the bons by, all to goe for use as hereafter,
then Cutt these too sids of the pig, for 4 Collers
Lay it by in a Cloath to dry it,
and gett these herbs to seson it, and spices
sweet mariarum winter savory parsly sorell and a
Litell tender saige Leves
stripe these and shred them so small as to bee but
like the spices, beaten, which must bee
nutmege Cloves
mace a few Cloves of peper, shred in,
mix all these together
According as it will Answer your tast
puting salt allso to it
then stow these herbs and spices
in the in side of each of the quartors,
Roling of it in thin Rolles—
then Role them up for Collers,
keeping that for out side
which was Cutt through in the middell
because it is the evenest,

then sow them with prety bigg whit thred,
Draw it through a Littell whit wax,
then sew them Close a bout in thin holand baggs,
put the same seasoning into the ears and
mouth and neck of the piggs head —
sowing it up allso in a thin fine Cloath,
while your collare [is] geting thus Redy,
Lett your Liquor bee
sett one a skillet Rather Deep than broad
Put in 3 quarts or a gallan of water,
3 qr of whit win,
a pint of vinegar
a good spunfull of hole peper
salt, enough too season it very high but not to salt,
because thus too bee boyled too a Jelley after wards
put 3 slised nutmegs Cloves and mace,
According as you Like it,
putt allso a bundle of sweett herbs, as winter savory,
sweet margurum,
put in allso the bons boyled and scim it, and
when the bons are enough boyled take them out
and put in the heed,
and the Collers and boyle them till tender,
then take them up in sum flat dish or plate,
then boyle the Liquor a bout a qr of an houer,
after that is out
then take out the bunch of herbs,
and poore it into sum earthen pot,
next morning take off the Cases from the
Collers and heed

and put them into an erthen vesell that you
intend to keep them in,
standing up on end, and the hed in the midell,
if the Liquor bee jellyed then sett it one and
warme it till it bee desolved
when so pore it upon the Coller
there must bee enough to Cover it,
if it bee not jelyed it must bee boyled againe,
and when Cold
pore it one as beefore —

These Larger piggs there harts Liver and Inwards will make a very fine puding thus ordered

[106]

Par boyle the Liver
breke it in a morter with yeolks of eggs
a few spunfulls of Creme, sum spice and
a Littell salt,
and worke it so together,
then putt into it sum shred savary herbs
as before in the pigg brann,
and beefe sewett very small —
roule this up with the yeolke of an egg:

Take a sasaige
and put it into the Call of a brest of Vele
and scald a Cloath and ty one the top of it,
and so boyle it,
and make it into Litell balls
and boyle them in a skillett,
with a Littell muten broath,
without either Cloath or Calle—
If you Like it, you may omit these and put Corants
and a Littell suger,
if so butter with wine and suger must bee the sauce,
if savory herbs, nothing but beat butter up—
you must shred the hart and other Inwards
with the sewitt—

Brawn, *the muscle or flesh of animals as food: a swine as fattened for the table.*
Collared *(cookery), rolled up and tied with a string, as a piece of meat from which the bones have been removed, a fish, brawn, etc.*
Caul *(cookery), the fatty membrane investing the intestine.*

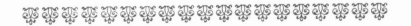

Too make a Fregasy of Chicken
[108]

Take your Chicken flea [flay] them and
Cutt them in peces
and boyle them gently in butter
with a bunch of sweet herbs,
after thay have bin a prittey while in,
putt sum good broath to them,
and when allmost enough, a gill of white wine
then take the yeolks of 4 or 5 eggs,
and sum shred parsley
1/2 a nutmeg grated
and sum juce of Lemon
but if you have not that 2 or 3 spunfulls of vinegar
beate them well together,
and when the other is enough, put this to it
sturing it up and downe together a Litell while
you may putt mushrons to it, and slised Lemon,
this is for 4 Littell biskets
putt a bitt or 2 of butter too the eggs and
other things
when you mix them together—

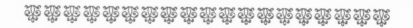

Too make a Collwort or Cabidg Puding

[115]

Take a pound of beefe and 1/2 a pound of suett
shred them small
season them with peper salt nutmegs sweet herbs
work it up with some yeolks of eggs,
boyle it in a Collwort or Cabidg Leafe
when it is boyled putt in sum butter and eat it —

Too Tost Veall

[129]

Take the Legg or neck
Cutt it into thin peices, the neck into Joynts
then Chop it a Litell
hang it to tost before the fire,
all the while kepe it floured with
peper
salt
very small shred parsly
grated bred
a Littell nutmeg
when it is hard tosted sarve it up with gravey sauce —

Too Dress a shoulder of muten with oystors

[119]

Take it Raw and stuf it
with oystors parboyled in there one [own] Liquor
then Rost it and have in Redynes
butter
white wine
sampher
capers
oystors
parsly good handfull Choped small,
a Littell time and sweet margarum, all Choped small
and sum grated nutmegs
when thay are boyled
put in a good Dele of minced Lemon,
and Lay in the shoulder of mutton
and put in the sauce to it,
and Lay Lemon slised one the top of the mutton,
and garnish with Lemon orinumbers and Capors
doe not put the butter till you put in the Lemons,
but boyle in sum tops of sparagrace with
youre things
put the gravey of the meat too it—

A White fancy of veall

[128]

Take youre velle and
Cutt it in Indiferent thin peces,
Chop it a Littell
Dredge it well with flouer,
then fry it with butter brownish
then putt a Littell weke broath
which you may stew it in a prity while,
then beat the yeolks of 4 eggs
4 or 5 spunfulls of thick Creme
and a Littell nutmeg,
when it is well beaten putt it too the fregasy,
and shake it well over the fire with a bitt of butter
you may Lard the velle if you plese —

Lard, *to insert small strips of bacon before cooking.*

[*Fried veal*]

[130]

take a brest of vele and Lay it in whit wine,
the flesh side Dounwards
Dip it in freter batter,
and fry it in fresh butter,
and put a great dele of Crispe parsly one it —

[BEVERAGES]

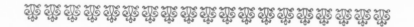

Too Make White Hipochrists

[2]

Take a gallan of sack:
and putť in too tow puter pots
on oz of very good Cinomon well brused
6 nutmegs 2 oz of Colleandr seed and
1/2 a qt of an oz of long peper all peal
but not too small,
severally 2 pounds of the best Refined shugger and
a Rase or 2 of ginger thin shred,
put all these things in to the sacke,
sum into one pot sum in the other
and so Lett them steepe together
sturing of it now and then,
with that which may ketch to the botom,
for an houre or too,
then put into it 1/2 a pint of new milke
sum into one pot and sum into an other,
and Lett it Steep
with sturing of it as before a Litell time,
then hang youre hepoikrist bagg upon a stafe
with sum stick at the uper end of the bagg,
and then put in to it youre hipochrists and
Lett it Run softly throu the bagg,
thus don twise or thris,
Leting it Run softly till it bee Cleare
the oftener you Run it the Clerer it will bee,
so put it into a botell, and stop it very Close,
you may Lett strong bere Run through 2 or 3 times,
and it will make a very plesant Drinke —

Hippocras. *This wine takes its name from the ancient Greek physician Hippocrates, indirectly, because it is filtered through a strainer of cotton, linen or flannel known as Hippocrates sleeve. A 1601 comment: "The wholesomest wines be such as have run through a strainer or Ipocras bag, and thereby lost some part of their strength." So Hippocras became "a cordial drink made of wine flavored with spices, formerly much in vogue."*

Rase of ginger, *apparently the same as a race of ginger, from* racine, *meaning* root. *Here it means a piece of ginger root thinly shredded. One of Guli Penn's eye cures has the sentence "Take a race of good ginger and pare it clean & rub it on a wheatstone to make a powder of it."*

Long pepper, *"the tree that beareth long pepper hath no similitude at all with the plant that brings black and white Pepper: some have deemed them to grow all on one tree: which is not consonant to truth: for they grow in Countries far distant one from another." p. 1539,* Gerards Herbal.

Too Make Hipochrists

[55]

Take 6 quarts of the best sacke and
put into it one oz of the best Cinomen in pouder
one oz of Cloves beaten in pouder,
in to it 2 1/2 pound of suger beten to pouder,
and brue it in 2 flagons well all together,
and then put in a bagg 2 or 3 grains of muske
or Ambergrece,
then put all youre Liquor in and when youre
Liquor hath once Run quite throw it,
put into the bagg a pint of milke
and put over in to the bagg youre Liquor again,
and so as many times till it com to bee Clere —

A Way too make Cydor

[92]

Take Brimston 2 oz
malego Resone 4 pound
mace Cinomon of each 1/2 an oz:
of nutmegs a 1/4 of an oz:
with a quart of wheat only the huske beat of
as for furmaty
all these hang in a barell of cydor —

Brimstone, *former common vernacular name for sulphur.*
Frumenty, furmente, furmety, *a dish made of hulled wheat boiled in milk, and seasoned with cinnamon, sugar, etc. Mentioned 1400 in* Morte Arthur.

Too Culler Cydor

[94]

Take elder berys and strain them,
and put the juce a mong the Cydor,
it maketh it Loock Like Clarett
and will Corectt the windiness —

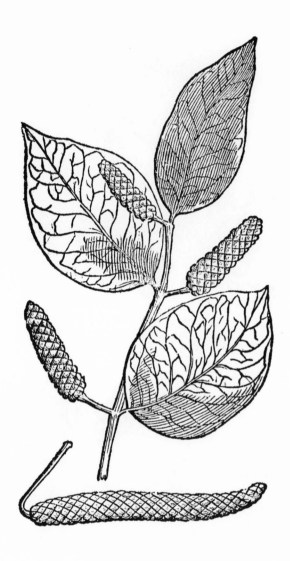

Piper longum.
Long Pepper.

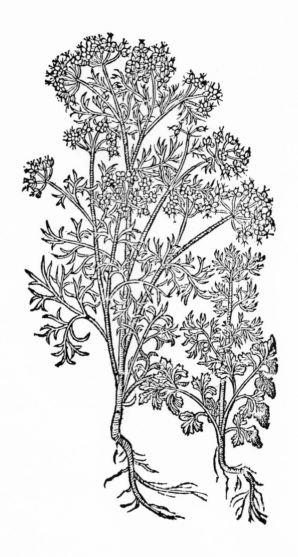

Coriandrum.
Coriander.

[*Apple beer*]

[95]

stamp apels and strain them as usuly for Cyder,
then take the Liquor and warm it
and put it upon the malt,
then when it is Com throu boyle it,
and then worke it Like other bere,
when it is put into vesells put 3 pound of hard suger
in to the quantaty of an hogsheed,
a few hops should bee boyled in it—

Too Make Burtch, by a Freind at the Clift in Lewis

[99]

Bore a hole through a burtch tree and
putt in a faset,
and putt sumthing under,
and when tis full boyle it of every 2 days
with 2 pound of white sugger too a gallan,
and when it is allmost Cold,
worke it up with a Littell yeist,
then put it up in Vesells
obsarve that the time to sane it in is in March
and at the begining of Aprill
if it bee a forward spring it will scarse Run
at all Aprill

*In his journal of a trip through Sussex in 1672 William Penn men-
tioned two Friends, John Ellis and Widow Akehurst, who lived at
the Cliff near Lewes. "William Penn's Journal: Kent and Sussex,
1672." PMHB, 68 (1944), 427 n.*

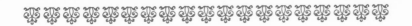

The Lady Oxendons too make Couslip and Marigold wine

[102]

Take 2 gallans of spring water
too which put 4 pound of Lofe suger,
and Lett them boyle gently one houer
then take a peck of flours
bruse them in a Morter,
and when the Liquor is blood warm
put the flouers into it
with the Juce of a Lemon
then take 3 spunfulls of yeist with
6 spunfulls of the Liquor
and beat it well together,
then put it to the other Liquor and
Lett them stand five Days,
then strain it out hard and put it out into a barrell,
after it is done working stop it Close
and Lett it stand a month or more
then draw it into bottells,
after 6 weeks boteling it will bee fitt to drinke,
keep it a year or Longer,
the larger the quantaty is made at a time the
beter the wine will be —

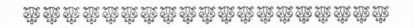

Too make a pritey sort of mede too keep too months

[107]

Take 10 quarts of spring watter and Lett it bee hot
then put in a quart of honey
and a pound of Lofe suger
Lett it boyle together till no scum Rises
which as it dus must bee taken off
it may boyle about 1/2 an houer,
then pore it forth in too the vesell,
or what you desire too keep it in,
and wring into it the juce of 4 Lemons
put in peell and all,
20 cloves
2 Rase of ginger
2 or 3 springs of Rosmary,
and when it is allmost cold make sum tostes and
spred one them
2 spunfulls of good ale yeist put them in warm,
so Lett it stand 4 or 5 days then bottell it off,
you may drinke it in a weeke after it is botteled,
and it will keep 3 months in the winter,
it must bee not stoped before it has dun workin —

Too make saige Wine

[116]

Take 25 quarts of spring water and boyle it
and Lett it stand
till it is a Littell more then blood warm
take 25 pound Raisons, Clene picked and shred
and 1/2 a bushall of the best Red saige
and so shred it allso
then put the fruite and saige into warme water,
then take a pint of ale yeist and put ther too,
and Cover it warme and Lett it stand 7 days
sturing it once a day
then strain it and put it into a Runlett,
Lett it stand a weeke or more
then putt too it a quart of malig sack,
bottell it putting a Littell suger in eatch bottell,
I think it the best way to put the sack in the bottells
and so too fill them up with saige wine
it may bee drunk in a month or 6 weeks
but it will keep good a yeare
in this manner, you may make Cowslipe wine
only allow a bushall of Cowslips in sted of 1/2 a
bushall of saige —

Runlett (*rondelet*), *a cask or vessel of varying capacity, small, a
pint to 4 gallons, large, 12 to 18 1/2 gallons.*

Too make Couslip Wine

[120]

Too every gallan of water . .
add 2 pound of good whit shuger,
boyle them together at Lest an houer,
then taking of [off] the scum,
sett it too Colle till it bee hardly blood warme,
then take too evry gallan 2 oz of Cittorn or Lemon,
which must bee well beaten,
with a quantaty of yeist fitt to sett it at worke,
too 6 or 7 gallans I think wee use to put in 1/2 a pint,
but of that more or Less too youre Discretion
or acording as the yeist is new or stale
make a great brown toast hot spred over with yeist —
putt the toast with the syrrup and yeist,
beaten as a fore said into the Liquor
and so Lett it stand and work 2 days and a night or 2
According as you find it worke
if you find it worke not kindly
stur it about with a Ladell very well
for a qr of an houer
which will very much help it,
after it hath stood the time to worke
Take too 6 gallan
1/2 a peck of Couslip flouers
put into a bagg fitt for the purpose
made of Corse white Cloath Called bollster
put it into a well sesoned vesell,
if it hath had Latly wine in it the better,

44

with a peece of Led or waite a bout 3 or 4 pound
in the bottom of the
bagg too keep the flouers downe,
then put in the Liquor,
to which add to over a gallan
a pint of white wine,
then put to it a Lemon or 2 Cutt in 1/2
then bung up the Caske, Close,
Leving only a Littell vent hole open
one the top of the Caske nere the bung
and so Lett it stand a month or 5 weeks
then draw it out into bottells,
and Lay it up in the sand,
in bottelling of it wee use to put in a
Lumpe of sugger about as bigg
as a Large nuttmegg in to eatch bottell,
this will keep good 9 or 12 months
but it may bee drunke of in a weeke or tow—

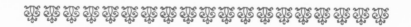

Too make small meed

[127]

Take 6 quarts of watter and warme it
one quart of the finest hony,
stur very well,
one Lemon and a qr of a pound of nuttmegs
sett it one the fire
and Lett it boyle till the scum is Black,
then take it of the fire and Colle it,
and when it is Luke warme,
 put yeist too it into a stand or spickett pot
and at the 4 day draw it into bottells,
Corke them Close
keep it a fortnight or 3 weeks in sand before
you Drinke it,
this will keep good 3 months —

Too mak Couslip wine

[136]

take a peck of Couslips and
a gallan of Runing water
4 pound of maligo Resons,
put Couslips and Resons a stepe in the watter 9 days
then strain it
and put the Clerest in to bottells
put a Lump of Lofe suger in to each bottell,
stop them Close
this will bee Redy to drinke in 3 days

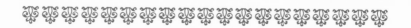

Too make gosbery wine or of any other fruit

[139]

Take to every gallan of gousberys
A gallan of watter,
bruse the gosberys and pore the water one them,
Lett it stand a weeke straining it often,
[add] as many pounds of suger
as gallans of [gosberys]
then Lett it Run through a gelly bagg:
tunn it up
you may boyle it in a furnis,
in a fortnight or 3 weeks you may drinke it —

Tunn, *a cask or barrel for wine, ale, beer, etc. Anglo-Saxon found as early as A.D. 725.*

∑ BAKED GOODS ∑

Too Make Naple Bisketts

[3]

Take one pound of fine shuger
3/4 of a pound of fine flouer,
youre shuger must bee serched
and the flouer sifted over 2 or 3 tims,
6 eggs whits and yeolks—beat them a while,
then put in your shuger and flouer and
temper them well,
and put in a grain of muske, and a
Littell Rose Water,
then buter youre mols thin over and so put them in,
and bake them in oven heated as for manchets,
you must not goe to breke your eggs till youre
oven is hott—

Getting the lumps out of sugar took up a good part of the cook's time in early days. No granulated, no confectioners' sugar. It might be loaf sugar or sugar broken up, but the cook must always pound it and put it through a sieve (sears it through a search) fine enough for her recipe.

Mols. *Mola was a salt cake, named perhaps from its shape, for the word also means millstone. It was anciently a cake made of grains of spelt coarsely ground and mixed with salt. A 1621 quotation: "This mole, lump or seasoned dough . . " comes close to Guli Penn's use of the word. By mol in this recipe Guli means the uncooked biscuit dough cut in shape ready for the oven. We need a word for this. Let us take* mol *back into the language!*

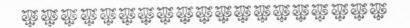

Too Make Mackerouns

[16]

Take a pound of fine suger beaten serced [sifted]
and a pound of Allmonds, blanched.
beat youre Almons in a stone morter with a Littell
Rose water,
then strain youre suger and beat them to gether,
till they bee well tempered,
then put them in a puter dish,
and sett them on a few Colls
but keep them sturing that thay do not burne —
to the dish take the yeilks of 14 eggs,
beaten too froath,
and wett them againe with the froath of the eggs,
then make them upon wafars
and bake them in an oven heated for manchets —

A **macaroon** *was the same thing in Penn's day that it is today.*

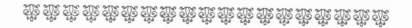

Too Make Puffs

[22]

Take a pound of the best Refined suger, beat it
serce [strain] it throug a fine Lane sive [linen sieve],
then put it in a fine marble morter,
you must have a fine wood pestell,
then take 5 whits of egs and beat them to a froath,
put sum of this froath to the suger,
Lett one allwais grind it Round with the pestell,
one way never Altering it,
put in by degrees allmost all the froath of the eggs,
and Continue grinding it, one houre or better,
then take a Littell Ambergrece,
and a Littell Muske,
put it in a spoun and mingle it with a Littell
Rose watter,
then grind it a Littell a bout with youre suger,
then put in 1/2 a spunfull of Aniseed,
and as much Caruway seed,
and stir them too gether with youre suger
you must have redy a py plate scoured
Clene with sand
then take a Littell butter And wash it in Rose Water,
and then Rubb youre plate with a Cloath and
sum of the butter
you must bee sure you have not to much one
youre plate —
for that will yallow the side of the puff,
when it is so grinded, as a bove written,
then take the sugar so grinded, as a bove written

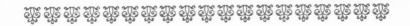

and Drop in drops—
all over the plats,
then put them in an oven, after pyes,
you must be sure the oven bee not too hott—

Musk and ambergris, *costly substances believed to have medicinal value. They are mentioned in the* Howard Housekeeping Books *of 1481; Baker Gesner's* Jewell of Health *(1576) instructs, "adde both musk and ambergrece." Mrs. Penn's recipes frequently call for these ingredients.*
Musk, *a substance secreted in a gland of the male musk-deer. Now used as a perfume base, also in medicine as a stimulant.*
Ambergris, *a wax-like substance of marbled, ashy color, found floating in tropical seas, and as a secretion in the intestine of sperm whales. Used in perfumery; formerly in cookery.*

Too Make suger Cakes

[24]

Take 3 pound of white flouer,
one pound of suger
a nutmeg
a blade or 2 or mace
4 eggs 2 of the whits being out
butter all most a pound,
2 spunfulls of Rose water,
a grain of muske,
so temper them all together,
and bake them in an oven as for Manchets—

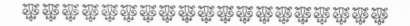

Too Make Allmon Cake

[25]

Take a pound of allmons, Blanch them
in Cold water
then with a knife slise them as thin as you Cann
then put a pound of fine suger beat and sifted
to the almonds
and 1/2 an oz of Corawa seeds, brused
2 spunfulls of rose water,
a grain of muske,
a grain of ambergrece
1/2 a handfull of fine flouer,
temper them together with the froath of the
white of an egg
and gem dragon Layd in Rose watter,
as much of the one as the other,
so stur them till thay are moyst,
lay them one a Maser, in the maner of
a Round Cake
So bake them in an oven heat as for suger Cakes—

Gem dragon, *possibly gum dragon* (*see #107*).
Gum dragon, *dragant, adragant, a gum teagacath. Mentioned in English literature as early as 1265. In 1704 the London Gazette referring to a ship's cargo mentioned "Gum Arabeck, Gum Dragant, etc."*
Mazer, mazre, **maser,** *a bowl of maple wood, found in English usage as early as 1290.*

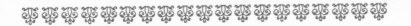

Too Make Bisketts

[30]

Take a pound of shuger and as much flour —
put to it as much Rose Water
as an egg shell will hold
and 4 or 6 eggs but halfe the whits,
temper and beat them well, while the oven is heting,
you may put in a grain of muske
one [or] too spunfulls the one of Coliander seeds,
the other of Caraway seeds,
and Lett the oven bee heted as for Manchets —

*Even today the English **biscuit** is what Americans call a cookie.*

Too Make Mackroons

[31]

Take a pound of Refined suger beaten very smale
a pound of almonds, well watered, and Dryed
and beat 2 whites of eggs, and take the froath
and put too it in to the Almons, as thay are beating:
till thay are well beate, then put the sugar in,
and stur them together,
and if you thinke good a graine of muske
make them upon masers,
and bake them in an oven as hott as for
suger Cakes —

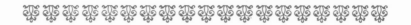

Too Mak Suger Cake the Best

[35]

Take 3 pound of the best fine flower Dryed
and Dubell sifted,
and too pound of Lofe Suger
and mingle them well together,
then putt in 4 yeolks of eggs,
and better then a qr of a pint of Rose water,
and then mingle them with the flouer
you may Desolve a Littell muske or Ambergrece
in the suger,
then putt in a Littell butter
as much as will make it up into a past,
soo Rolle out then bake them in a quick oven,
but Lett it not scorch,
sift a Litel Puer suger one them,
when you have made Lett them not bee
made too thick —

Too mak Pasty Crust for the tops of plum floridine

[37]

Take 2 handfulls of fine flouer Dryed
2 eggs one white out
1/2 a pound of sweet butter,
work thes in to a past not kneling of it,
nor brakeing of it
but Roule it out for youre use—

Floridine, *probably same as florentine, i.e. tart or pie.*

An other:

Take a gallan of flouer
and putt to it a pound of beefe suett shred very small
and 1/2 a pound of butter,
a Littell salt,
youre suett and butter must bee putt in the flouer
and Rubed when it is Dry as you doe a great Cake,
and then you must put in as much Cold water as
will wet it
in a Diferent Limberence,
and you must putt in the yeolks of 4 eggs—

Limberence, *limberness, pliability, pliancy.*

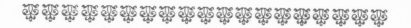

Too make a Parsnep puding

[46]

Take sum parsneps and
boyle them till thay bee very soft,
then mash them very small
and picke out the hard peces,
then put to it sum grated breed or flouer,
and a good many Corrants
sum nuttmeggs and a Litell suger,
and when you have mixed them together
putt too an Indeferett quantaty
the yeolks of 4 or 5 eggs:
Wett it with Creme till it bee as thin as batter,
and then fry them quick,
if you will boyle it you must not make it so thin
and boyle it in a Cloath spred with butter,
when it is boyled melt sum butter with
sack and shuger
for the sam—

Too make French Bred

[48]

Take 1/2 a bushall of mele if it bee good,
ale yeist a poringer full,
wett it with warme water, but not boyled
knede it not too stife —
sett it by the fire 2 or 3 houers Covered
with a Cloath
then mold it in to Loves,
and Lett it stand till the oven bee hott,
wash it with the yeolke of an egg
and a spunfull or 2 of bere,
Lett it stand an houre and a halfe —

A Cake

[51]

Take a pecke of fine flouer
put to it a bout an ounce of Caraway seeds,
fine grated nutmegs
then 3 pound of butter broke in small peces in
to the flouer,
untill it bee Like white bred Crums,
then put a pint of Creme and 3 pints of yeist
strained into it,
and mix it well,
then put 3 pounds of Caraway Comphets in
only Reserve too strew one the top when the
Cake is made —

Comfit, comphet, *usually a small round or oval mass of sugar enclosing a caraway seed, almond, etc., a sugar plum. Found in a manuscript as early as 1334.*

Too Make Whigs

[52]

Take 1/2 a peck of flouer by mesure,
then take a pound of butter
and breke it into it with youre hands,
the quantity of an oz: of nutmegs,
mace and sinomen together in fine pouder,
3/4 of a pound of Caraway comfets,
a pint and a 1/2 of yeist,
the same of milke, it must bee blood warme,
be suer you Do not over bake them—

Wig, *wedge shaped cake, a kind of bun or small cake made of fine flour (1376–1888).*
1688: "Wigg is White Bread moulded long ways, and thick in the middle."

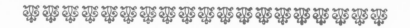

To Make a Cake

[53]

Take too 1/2 a peck of flouer
one oz Cinomon as much mace
and as much grated nutmegs
a 1/4 of an oz of sugger, all finly beaten,
2 pound of suger with a Littell salt,
mingle all these well together with the flouer
then breke in 2 pound of fresh butter,
then put in 4 pounds of Corants —
1/2 a pint of ale yeist,
of sacke and creme sack 1/2 a pint,
Lett all bee Cold then kneed it
and Lay it before the fire to Rise Raped in
a hot Cloath —
when the oven is hott Ice the kake all over
with Rose water butter and 1/2 a pound of suger
Lett the Rose Water bee warme —

Too make a seed Cake

[54]

Take 2 pound and a 1/2 of Allmonds
blanch them in Cold water
then beat them in a stone Mortar,
with a Littell Rose Water to keep them from oyling,
then mingle them with a pound and 3/4 of Lofe shuger
beaten very fine,
with a Littell of youre suger sum ambergrece and
mix with youre allmonds,
take 6 whits of eggs beat them to a froath,
Lett them Stand a Littell
then take the froath,
Clene from the oyle as you Can,
and mingle them very well with youre Allmonds,
then sett them one a Chafing dish of Coalls
and dry it
sturing them all the while for fere of burning,
thay must bee drye . .
Take 1/2 a peice [peck?] of flouer and putt into it
a Littell salt,
3 pints of good ale yeist
you must have in Redyness youre Creme hot that
must bee not more then blood warme,
then put in too youre flouer
as much of youre Creme as will make it a stife past,
you must strain out youre yeist,
with 6 spunfulls of sacke,
when you have the past, Lay it before the fire
with a Dubell Cloath over it,

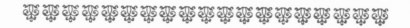

Lett it Ly so an houer,
then work into the past 2 lb and a 1/4 of
fresh butter,
put your past in Litell peces and
mingle youre Allmonds with it
pull your past in peces 3 times,
then strew a pound of Caraway Comfets
all but a handfull and that you must Resarve
to strew upon the top of the Cake
the proprotion will make 3 Caks
take py plats then Lay the past one youre papers,
One [in] a Lump not so broad as the plats
by 2 Intches
then strow youre Comfets one the top of the Caks
and Dubell Refined suger,
then presently sett them into the oven
about an houre will bee enough
mingle a little saffron with youre Creme—

Too make a buttered Lofe

[63]

Take a good Dele of wheat flouer,
as many yeolks of egs as you thinke fitt
a Litell yeist
butter
suger
cloves
mace
a Littell salte
work all these together
breke it in to small peces and that will make it short,
then bake it well and Cut it in the midell
and buter it with sweet buter and suger
then Lay the 2 halfes to gether
and keep it warme by thee till you eat it—

Too make thin oat Cakes

[73]

It must bee made with oaten meale steped [steeped]
all night in pump water,
and bake it the next morning
pore in the batter upon a stove with a brass Ladell

Stove, *not the confectioners drying box here, but a closed box to
contain burning fuel.*

Too Make oat Cakes

[74]

Take a 1/4 of a peck of flouer,
a pint of yest if it bee new
1/2 a pint of it to bee sad,
and the Liquor Resonable hot, but not boyled,
and when the Dow is made
Cover it for a qr of an houer to Rise—
and when thay are Could,
out Lay the Caks upon a Linen Cloath [or] woulen,
and Cover them Warme with a Cloath an other qr
of an houer
and then bake them when thay have Lain a while—
then turne them once or twise—

Too Make Allmon Caks

[75]

Take 1/2 a pound of the best Allmonds and
blantch them in Cold water all night,
then in the morning Cut out all the spots
that Look yellow,
beat them in a stone mortor, very fine—
then beat them with 1/2 a pound of suger till thay
bee well mingeled,
then take the wits of 4 eggs, beaten to froath
put the froath too the Allmonds,
mixing them well together in a dish
sett the Dish one hot Coalls,
sturing it till it grow thick,
then put them one wafers
when you beat them, put them in sum Rose water,
and sum muske,
put them not in too hott an oven
lest thay Culler to much,
bake them one plats—

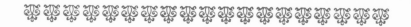

Too make mass Cakes

[79]

Take a pound of youre finest flouer and
dry it in an oven,
then take 1/2 a pound of fin Lofe suger, beat it fine
and a bout a qr of an oz of mace shred very small,
mingle all that together with a very Litell salt,
then have Redy a qr of a pound of sweett butter—
Leasarly melted, upon a Chafing Dish of Colls
with 2 or 3 spunfulls of rose water,
and when it is throu melted take it from the fire
and Lett it setell the butter milke from the
buter to the
bottom in the dish
so pore in the Clere of it
till you find it prity passable
to worke and so kned it to gether a Littell
and make them out into Cakes,
and Cut them with a glase,
bake them on buter [pewter?] plats,
and so prick them
youre oven must bee as hot as for biskacks—

Too Ice a great Cake the Wood street way

[82]

When you have baked youre Cake have Redy sum
fine Lofe suger
beaten finly so wett it in sum rose water very well,
so beat it in a morter till it grow Clere
then take a fether or tuff of silke and
wett the Cake all over,
then sett it in the oven a Litell time,
doe this 3 tims and it will bee a fine thin Ice —

Too make Itallyon Biskett

[85]

Take serched suger and the white of an egg
a Littell ambergrese
a Littell muske
beat these apart in a Alliblaster morter,
then put in a Littell Aniseed finly beaten,
mingle all these together
and make them up in Littell Loafes Like Cracknells,
put them in an oven as hot as for manchets,
bake them on plats,
when thay bee risen high take them out
and remove them one other plats —

Cracknells, *a light crisp kind of biscuit of a curved or hollowed shape.*
(1523): "When the plate is hote, they cast of the thyn paste thereon
and so make a lytle cake in maner of a crakenell, or bysket."

The Lady Maradays Cake

[91]

Take a strike [strict] gallan of flouer
too each gallan of flouer three gallans of Corants,
one pound of Resons of the sonn stoned,
a pint of Rose water,
a pint of Creme
a pint of ale yeist
a pound of butter,
beat the salt out of it in Rose water,
then breke in to the Cake, 4 oz of fine suger,
one oz of Cloves, nutmeg and Mace beaten small,
mingle all these to gether,
and graspe it in youre hand
till thay are all parffectly mingeled
make it up Lite
add to each gallan,
of eggs one white,
one grain of muske and Ambergrece,
grind it with youre suger
Lett youre oven bee very quick but not scortching—

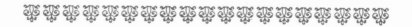

Too make Ginger Breed

[96]

Take 3 pound of treckell
and as much flouer as it will need,
mingle with the flouer a 1/4 of a pound of
beaten ginger,
and a qr of Coraway Coriander and Anis seeds,
a Littell brused
and 3 grated nutmegs
1/2 a pound of suger,
then make it into a stife past,
and beat it with a Rouling pinn, to make it Lite,
it must bee baked in tinn pans which must bee
a Littell buttered,
as sone as thee take it out of the oven
just dip it in to scalding hot watter,
and put it into the oven againe, and Lett it,
If thee hast any oring or Lemon peele
slice sum very thin in to the treckell
3 or 4 days before thou makest the ginger breed

Treacle, *molasses.*

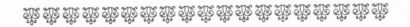

Too make Elizabeth Kimbols Cake

[97]

Take 6 pound of flouer well Dryed,
6 pound of Corants
one pound of Raisons of the sun stoned and cutt
1/2 a pound of dats Cut,
oring and Lemon and Citorn,
spice and parsoms what you plese
10 yeolks of egg 3 whits
Crem a quart,
butter 2 pound
balme a quart
sack 10 spunfuls,
Rose water 6 spunful,
3/4 of a pound of Lofe sugger,
take youre fruit flouer suger and mix together,
beat youre eggs with youre Creme and strain
them [with] youre sack and rose water,
melt youre butter and putt youre Creme too it,
put youre flouer and other Ingredions into a
large earth pann—
put them up the sides with a hole in the midell
then take youre bame eggs buter and Creme and
put them into the midell of youre flouer,
and only strow one sum flouer with youre hand,
and set it down to the fire till it rise over
then take it up and mix it well together
and set it doen again, till it rise
have your coffen Redy buttered fill it 1/2 full
set it in the oven an houer and 3/4

Parsoms (*persimmons?*) *plum-like American fruit described* (*1612*) *by John Smith.*
Balme, *name of some fragrant garden herbs, i.e. balm gentle or balm mint (melissa officinalis).*

Too Make Portingall Cake

[100]

Take Lofe suger a pound,
beat it and search it throu a sive
with a pound of flouer very fine that is well aired
and then take a pound of butter,
and wash it well in Rose water,
then worke it well with youre hands till it bee soft,
and strew the flouer and suger in bye degrees,
till it bee 1/2 in, still working it with youre hands
then put 6 yeolks of eggs and 4 whits
then by degrees worke in the other 1/2 of the
suger and flouer,
and when the oven is hot,
putt in 2 spunfuls of Rose water
a pound of Corants
then have youre pans Redy butered
and fill them not almost 1/2 full
and sirup suger one them just as you set them
in the oven—

Too make that which is Called at Medstone, peene Breed

[109]

Take a pound of that which thay Call
Jurden Allmonds,
Lay them one Cold watter over nite
blanch them the next morning over fresh watter,
take them quick out as you blantch them
Lest thay part,
spred them one by one upon a fine Cloath,
upon a table,
Cover them with an other to dry them white,
have in Redyness, when you have sliced them,
a pound of dubell Refined suger finely beatten
and serched,
then with a knife slice youre Allmonds the short
way as thin as Lane
then have by a deep erthen or peuter bason,
put them in as you slice them,
strewing the fine suger one them,
still as you put in too keep them from
Cloding and oyling
thus doe till the hole pound of suger is mixed
with the almons
you must slice them upon new trenchers that have
not bin washed
with very sharpe knifes often scrape one knife
with the other

too sirupe off what sticks too them,
put to the suger and Allmonds
1/2 an oz of Caraway seeds, brused
2 spunfulls of damaske Rose watter,
a grain of muske and
a grain of Ambergreece grinded together with a
Littell fine suger
1/2 a handfull of very fine suger,
1/2 a handfull of very fine flouer, Dryed
temper all these together with the froath of a white
of an egg,
and gum dragon steeped in Rose watter,
as much of the one as of the other,
so stur them together till thay are moyst,
then Lay them upon a Masor,
in the maner of a round Cake,
Laying first a bottom,
opening the slices with a silver bodkin,
then lay a Rod a top
then bake it in an oven hott as for suger Cakes,
when thay are well Risen in the oven take them of
and Rub them with the froath of the white of an egg
Dusting them over with fine sugger in tifaney
then sett them in againe,
Lett them stand till thay are drye and Crispe,
thay must bee baked in sheets of tinn
the waffers must bee left Larger then the Cake,
and Dresed when baked with a pint of suggers—

Too make French Breed After Brigett Atkines nurses way— oaten bread

[111]

Too a potell of flouer a 1/4 of a pound of yeist . .
3 whits of eggs and a part of one yeolke,
1/2 a pint of milke or as much as will wett it,
mingle with the rest
and 1/2 a pint of wine and white wine veniger
but not so much as too Curde
and wett it as tender as may bee made up
dashing it with flouer that it stick not to
youre hands,
then Lay it one a Cloath too Rise
when its well risen this must not Lye to Long
Lest it bee soured
Leste it falle and not rise in the oven
which may bee prevented by working it together
while the oven is hott or redy—

Pottle, *a measure of capacity equal to 2 quarts.* (*1636 Plymouth Laws; 1788 Washington diary.*)

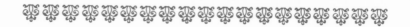

Too make the best Caraway Cakes

[143]

Take 1/2 a peck of flouer
4 pound of butter Rub fine in the flouer,
3 pounds of Caraway Comphets,
a pound of allmons, thin sliced,
1/2 a pint of sacke
4 eggs
a qrt of good alle yeist warm
and mix the yeist egs and sack
and Lett the oven bee hot and Redy before
it bee mixed
and put in the Allmons Citturn and Carawais—
when it is well mixed put it in the oven—

"**Caruwaie** seeds confected, or made with sugar into Comfits, are very good for the stomacke they helpe digestion, provoke urine, asswage and dissolve all windinesse: to conclude in a word, they are answerable to anise seed in operation and virtues." p. 1539, Gerarde's Herball (1636).

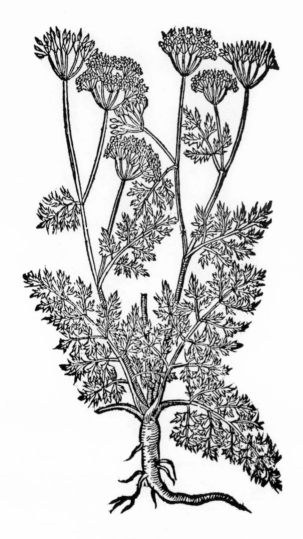

Carum, ſiue Careum.
Caruwaie.

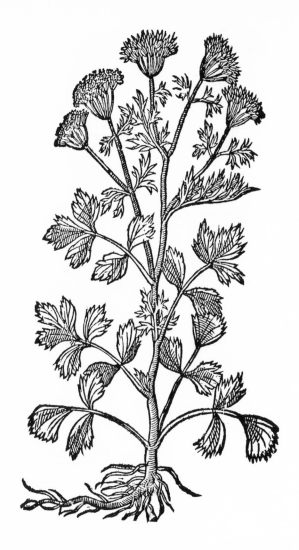

Aniſum.
Aniſe.

[CUSTARDS & PUDDINGS]

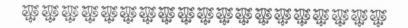

Too Make Snow Creme

[5]

Take a quart of Creme that is very thick, and
put it into a bole with 2 or 3 spunfuls of Rose water
and a Littell suger, then beat it with a spoune
and as the froath Rises take it of,
and Lay it in a dish till the dish bee full,
and that Ly high in the midell Like snow,
then sirupe the suger one the sids of the dish,
but Lett it not Coum up on the froth
for fere of waighing it doune.

Too Make Pudings

[10]

Take white bred slised very thin
then Lay the botom of the dish with Litell bitts
of sweet butter
and thin slices of bred,
with a few currants,
and a blade or too of mace —
then more butter,
and too or three Laine [layers] of bred
butter and Curants
in the maner that you make a dish of Apelils
[apples], with marrow,
so fill up youre dish with Custards,
stufe and backe it,
either in the oven or upon a pot of water,
slise in a few pipins when you bake it
or a Litell Rose water —

Too make Pluding

[11]

Take greated bred,
seson it with a Littell nutmeg and suger,
then rubb sweet buter one it till the bred bee moyst
with the butter,
then put in 2 eggs whits and all,
so wett it withe the eggs, milke or Creme
till it bee thin as batter,
so butter a dish and bake it
Lett it not stand too long in the oven,
for that will Dry it and spoyle it—

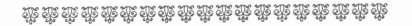

Too make a Hasty Puding
[12]

Take 1/2 a pint of milke
boyle it with a blade or tow of mase
sweeten it with sugger and thick it with grated bred,
beat 2 eggs
put a way one of the whits and a Litell rose water
with the eggs,
when you have put in the bred, put in the eggs
and at lest 1/2 a pound of butter
sett it one the fire Continuly sturing of it—
that it stick not to any part of the skillett,
Lett it boyle till the puding bee stife and
the butter seuor [drain off] from the breed
then clap a dish one top of the skillett,
and turn it quick into the Dish,
and it will hold propotion of a skillett,
as if it had ben baked in a pan swiming in butter
Stick it with Allmons and so sarve it up—

Hasty pudding, *a pudding made of flour or oatmeal stirred in boiling milk or water to the consistency of a thick batter. In U. S. made with Indian meal.*

An Other

[13]

Take apells shred them small as for freters,
temper flower with too eggs and milke prity thick
as you would a suett puding,
and make it full of the sliced apells,
buter youre pan and so bake it
when it is cold slise it,
and fry it,
and it is like apell pankecks
sum will putt in sum resons,
and cut it so soune as it Coms out of the oven,
spreding it with Butter

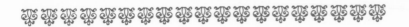

Too Make a soft Creme

[14]

Take a soft creme and set it over the fire,
and when it boyls put in the yeilk of 12 eggs, beten,
so Lett it boyle till it bee thick
then put it into cloath too whay it,
and hang it up,
when the whay is Dropt sarve it out,
sweeten it with shuger and a Littel Rose watter,
if you make it white you must take the whits of eggs
and make it as the other —

Whey, *the watery part of milk which remains after curd coagulates, especially in making cheese.*

Too make an Allmon Puding

[15]

Take a quartor of a pound of Allmonds
blanch them and beat them very small,
then take a qr of a pound of fresh butter,
melt it then temper youre Allmonds with it,
and a few Crums of bred —
the yeolks of too eggs
a few Crums of breed,
one or too spunfulls of Creme
sweetened with suger —
so put it in a dish made Like a florentine,
with a past
and bake it in a soft oven,
and so sarve it in —

Florentine, *used as early as 1567 to mean a kind of pie or tart,*
sometimes a custard made in paste (i.e. custard pie?). I think Mrs.
Penn is saying to cook the almond paste filling in a crust like a custard
pie.

Too Make a Hedg Hogg Puding
[17]

Take a pint of Creme,
and put an Nutmeg Cutt in quarters in to it
and sett it over the fire till it bee redy to boyle
then take it of and putt into it
1/2 a pound of beefe sewett shred very small
and the crums of a peny Lofe of white bred
7 eggs and 3 whits and 4 yeolks,
a Littel shugar tempered alltogether
wett a Cloath and putt youre puding in it,
and when it is redy too tye up,
put a few Resons of the sunn in it,
strew them Just in the midell,
and put it in all hast into a skillett of hot watter,
and Lett it boyle,
and then take it out of the Cloath,
and sticke it with almonds, blanched
and Cutt it in slices
and so sarve it in with butter and suger —
add too this sum Allmons beaten very fine,
and putt into the breed —

Too Make a Puding or Cheese Lofe

[29]

Take a gallan of new milk,
and make a tender Curd of it,
Lett it bee well Whayed [i.e. whey drained off],
then putt as much grated breed as curd
and 1/2 a pint of Creme,
the yeolks of 6 eggs:
temper these together, and sweeten them.
and then make them up in the fashion of manchets,
so bake them
then Cutt them a tope and buter them
puting muske in the butter, and a Little sacke—

Sack, *a general name for a class of white wines formerly imported from Spain and the Canaries; used at least as early as 1536. Markham's* English Housewife *(1623): "Your best Sacks are of Seres in Spaine, your smaller of Galicia and Portugall, your strong Sacks are of the Ilands of the Canaries and Malligo."*

Too make a Brown hasty puding
[66]

Take milk set it on the fire
then take grated [manchets] and stur it in
to the milk,
seson it with Cinomon, nutmeg salt rosmary
and suger
put in 4 or 5 eggs beaten in a Litell of the milk,
when it is boyled put it forth into a dish,
with a Litell buter all over it
then take a fire shovle Red hot
and hold it Close too it
till it Loock brown,
stick it with peces of blanched Allmons —

Too Make Allmon Butter

[69]

Take one pound of good almonds Blantched and
beten exseeding smalle, —
then having in Redyness fayre watter wherein the
crust of a manchet has bin boyled,
and a blade or too of mace
strain the beaten Almonds with the water,
then Sett it a Litell on the fire,
but Lett it not seeth,
then turn it with Red Rose water,
then Lay it thin one a Cloath
and Lett the whay Run through it,
and put the fore Corners of the Cloath [together]
and hang it one a tack to drain a day or too
seson it with suger and a Littell saffron and
Dish it out —

Too Make a Custad with Pistatus and Allmonds

[83]

Take a Quart of Creme and boyle it and
Cole it again
and put 7 or 8 eggs well beten
then take 20 pistatus [pistatios]
[put] them in warm water with 12 Allmonds
beat these well together and small with rose water
strain them through a course strainer
with sum Creme,
before you put in the ggs seyson it very well
with fine suger
and Ambergrece as a gret pins heed
1/2 as much muske,
when all these things bee well mingeled
put a dish one boyling water and put it in
and Cover it,
when it is backed stick it with a green
sittorn [citron] —
soften your sitorn in warm water to make it
tender and soft —

Too Make Gosbery Creme

[84]

Take a quart of green gosbery
put them in as much Cold water as will
Cover then —
then sweten it to youre tast,
then boyle them and Cover them till thay bee
all to mash —
then take the yeolks of 2 eggs or 3 new Laid
well beten with Rose water
and then stur them a mongst youre gosberys
then sett them over the fire a Litell to harden,
but take heed thay Courdle not,
you may put in 3 or 4 spunfuls of thick Creme,
and when it is thicke sarve it up
put it into an other Dish to sarve it in —

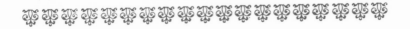

Too Make Allmon Butter

[87]

Take a pound and a 1/2 of best Jurdon Allmons
stepe them at Lest too days in Cold water
shifting the water twise a Day,
then take them out of the water and blanch them
then beat them exstremly,
first strain it with new milke
that none of the Juce remain,
take a quart of Creme and put the Juce in it
and sett it one Coalls in a skillet
with as much suger as will sweeten it and
1/2 a spunfull of rose water,
the yeolks of 8 new laid eggs well mixed together
Lett it bee set one the fire but suffered not to boyle
there will Rise a Curd which will bee very thick
which take of with a spone,
and Lett it run through a haire strainer
till the whay bee all out,
then with [?] youre Curd through a strainer
into the glass
with Ambergrece
so eate it —

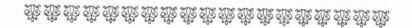

Too make an oring Puding sister Louthers way

[98]

Take 2 very good Civell [Seville] orenges,
Lay them in water,
then great them meat Rine and alle
put too them 10 eggs Leving out 2 whits,
the egs must not bee beaten,
3/4 of a pound of white suger
1/2 a pound of butter broken in Littell peces,
beat these too gether in a mortor
till tis all Like as it were Cureled,
putt it into a dish with sum Cold past
it must bee but 1/2 an houer a baking in
a quick oven,
Lay the peast thick at the botom and sids of the dish
and when the puding is in
Cutt sum strips of past and
Lay Crose the dish booth wais Like
Cheynor Worke—

Cheynor Worke, *i.e. China work, that is, resembling open work porcelain, as found in certain ornamental fruit dishes, luxuries of the period.*

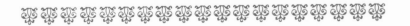

Too Make white Pudings

Take a pound of Allmond,
blanch them in Cold Watter
beat them fine in rose or oring flouer watter,
then take 16 eggs with 1/2 the whits putt a way
then mingle it with the allmonds
then putt 8 spunfulls of the oring flouer
watter to them
haveing first put in the watter and
a Littell muske and
Ambergrece a bout the bigness of a great pin
Then take a pound of white suger,
and 2 pounds of beefe suett, Cutt small,
then add the peils of 2 presarved oringes
2 of Lemons,
Cut them . .
then mix them all together with a pint of Creme
fill youre skinn, washed in milke and Rose watter,
I putt 2 or 3 spunfulls of grated breed or
naple bisketts
and Leve out 1/2 a pound of the suette
I thinke thay are too fatt elce—

Too make Lemon Creme

[114]

Take 4 great Lemons
chicp them and shred the Chips very small,
and put them into a silver poringer,
squesing to them the juce of the 4 Lemons
so Lett them steep for 3 houers,
then take the whits of 6 or 7 eggs
and the yeolks of 3 of them beaten well together,
and put to them the Lemon juce and pills
[rind, peels],
and a poringer and a 1/2 of watter
and a 1/4 of a poringer of Damaske Rose watter
or oring flouer water
and so stew them well together,
then strain it through a strainer of Cottenn
and season it sweet with Dubell refined suger
and a Littell muske and ambergrece,
then put it one a Chafing dish of Coalls
sturing it Continually
when it is Cold dish it up as you plese
It may bee made with juce of oringes if Lemons
bee too sharpe,
with either Lemons or oringes peiles
and taken at any time when trubeled with drith —

Drith, *obsolete form of dryth, dryness, thirst, drought.*

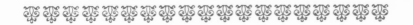

Too make otmell puding

[117]

Take 1/2 a pint of otmell and
scald it in a pint of new milke
and Lett it stand all night
the next day take 6 yeolks and two whits of eggs
beten with 3 or 4 spunfulls of Creme
stur it with the otmell and seson it with salt,
nutmeg and mace beaten small
and put in sum shuger and Rose water
then flouer a Cloath
then ty it up round and boyle it an houer,
then put it into a dish and pore butter on it —

Too make a Fansey of Apells

[118]

Take apells and boyle them very tender in a skillett
of watter,
then strain the pap of them, and put to it sum
yeolke of egg
sturing it well together,
and put in a spunfull or too of grated bred,
and a Littell Creme and suger,
and so mingle it all together,
then fry it in sweet butter,
you may putt in some juce of spinaige if you will
to Coller it when you mingle it—

Fancy, *something that pleases or entertains.*

Too make White Puding

[121]

Take a pound of Allmons blanch them in Cold water
beat them very fine in Rose or oring watter,
then take 16 eggs with 1/2 the whits put a way,
then mingle it with the Allmonds,
then put 3 spunfuls of oring flouer water too them
having 1st put in the water a Littell muske
and Ambergrece
about the bigness of a great pins heed,
then take a pound of white sugger,
2 pound of beefe suet Cutt small
then add the peels of 2 presarved oringes and
2 of Lemons,
Cutt them [small] then mix all together with
Creme then
fill there skinn which if you plese wash in milke
and Rose water
I put 2 or three spunfuls of grated bred or
Naple biskett
I Leve out 1/2 a pound of the suett for I think
thay are too fatt—

Common Sage.

[PRESERVES]

[JELLIES]

[CANDY]

To Make Harts horn Jelly

[1]

Take 4 oz of the shavings of harts horne
one oz of the shavings of Ivery,
Infuse it all night upon embers in a posett of
Runing watter,
with 1/2 a pound of Raisons of the sonne stoned,
with a Littell mace in an erthen pipkin,
in the morning boyle it up with a Litell saffron,
if you Like it a Littel Licorish and sum
opening Rooses,
if you plese serching it with a Litell [sugar]

Nothing could sound more medieval, remote, even incomprehensible than jelly made from shavings of hart's horn and ivory, infused upon embers in a posett and serched with sugar. But it is nothing strange— we eat it constantly. This is Guli Penn's recipe for gelatin, in a wording from another world. "Infuse it all night upon embers in a posett of Runing watter" means no more than "soak it all night in warm water"; the other ingredients are flavoring and fruit. **Serching** *means simply sprinkling or sifting sugar on it. The jelly identification suddenly dawns from reading a definition in the large* Oxford Dictionary of English: *"hartshorn jelly, a nutritive jelly made formerly from shavings of harts' horns, now from those of calves bones." The earthen pipkin, in cookery, is a small earthenware pot or pan.*

Too Presarve Oringes

[18]

Take youre oringes and picke out the Carnals
then Lay them in a Riner water [brine] 9 days,
Changing them twise a day,
then pare of the Rine [rind] very thin
then way them, with twise the waight of
suger or more,
putt a pint of water too every pound of sugger,
before you putt them together
boyle the oringes in faire water
Changing them in severall waters till the
Bitterness of the oringes bee taken a way:
then putt the suger waters and oringes together,
and Lett them boyle till the oringes bee so tender
as you may put a straw throw it,
then take them out, and Lett them boyle till it Jelley,
boyle it very fast,
take out youre oringes when thay are 1/2
boyled, a while
and put them in again
and so Lett them stand a day—

Too Presarve old Pippins

[19]

Take a pound of Apells and 3/4 of a pound of suger
1/2 a pint of water and as much white wine,
so boyle them one a soft fire—

Too Make Red Marmolet of Quinces

[20]

Take a pound of suger and
sum what more of Quinces,
slise the Quinces in thin slises
then putt a pint of water and a pint of
grated Quinces
putt them together and Cover them,
and boyle them soft
thay will bee Red enough—

Too make Past of Quinses of white marmolett

[21]

Take Quinces and boyle them in watter till
thay bee soft,
then peele them,
and take 3/4 of a pound of suger too a pound
of quinces,
Lett the suger bee so boyled too a Candy hight
then Coull them and give them a Wollup or tow,
so make them out in Cackes,
or putt them into glasses for marmolett —

Boil to a candy height, *See #28.*

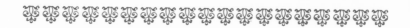

Too Candy Pipins
[26]

Take Pipins and pare them and Cutt them in halfes
and to a pound put 1/2 a qr of suger,
and as much water as will Cover them.
and Lett them boyle a Little together
till the suger doe goe through them,
and Lett them stand till thay begin to drye a top
then make a Candy for them and dip them in it,
and so dry them for youre use—

Too Make Vilot Cakes
[32]

Take the vilots and picke the leves
and take suger and put to it, a Litell water
and put to it the flouers
and boyle it together to a Candy
when allmost Cold Drop it—

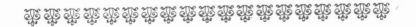

Too make Red past and Jelly of Quinces

[28]

Take a pound of quince cut in qr
and a pound of suger,
a pint of water,
Lett them boyle together till they Look
a bright Reed,
then take out the quince and way to a pound,
1/2 a pound of shuger
and boyle it to a highte,
and so put them together and give them a Wallop,
and make them out on plates—
take the Liquor of this quinces,
and put a quarter of suger too a pint,
and so boyle it to a Jelly—
and so put it in glasses for youre use
Lett sum Quince Carnalls [seeds] bee boyled in it—

Boil to a height, *i.e. to a candy height, means to the point of candying or crystallizing.*

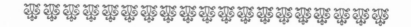

Too Make Lemon Cakes
[34]

Take a Lemon the peele, and Cutt it small,
then put it in a morter and
squese a Littell juce into it
and straine it through tifany,
then take Dubell Refined suger, and a Littell water,
a Littell Ambergris tyed in a Rag of tifany,
and sett it one the fire
and Lett it boyle to a Cundy hight,
then put in the juce & stur it together very well,
and Lett it bee almost Cold,
then drop it one a sheett of paper
Lett them stand one the fire,
and when thay are a Littell Drye turne —

Tiffany, *a kind of thin transparent silk; also a transparent gauze muslin, cobweb lawn. A fanciful word derived from Epiphany, perhaps referring to the miracle of its delicacy when invented about 1600.*

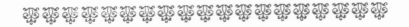

Too Presarve Churys in Gelley

[36]

Take green Gosberys and slice them on the side
that sum of the Liquor may Run out,
put them into a pot
and put to them 2 or 3 spunfulls of watter
stop the pot very Close,
and sett it into a skillett of water over the fire,
Lett them boyle till the gosbery Liquor bee
clere as watter,
then take it of of the fire, and strain the Liquor
too 1/2 a pound of Churrys, stoned, take
1/2 a pound of Dubell Refined sugger, small beaten,
strew sum suger at the botam of the skillett,
then Lay a Layer of Churyes
and after a Layer of suger, then a Layer of Churrys —
keep out a bout 3 oz of youre shuger too throw one
thm as thay boyle,
put to youre Churrys that Layd in the skillett,
6 spunfulls of the gusberys Liquor
then sett them one the fire and Lett them boyle
softly at first, till the suger bee melted,
after boyle them as fast as you Can
scuming them very well
observe that thay doe best when you doe but 1/2 a
pound at a time,
take them up and boyle your Liquor untill it Jeley:
when it will Jelly it will stick one youre spone,
then put them oute —

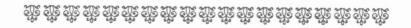

Too make Quidany of Red Corants

[39]

Take to one pint of the juce of Currants,
one quartor of a pint of the juce of Rasps
and to those you must put
one pound of fine Lofe suger—
beaten and sifted very fine,
boyle it to a gelly
and while it is hot put it out into glasses—

Quiddany, *a thick fruit syrup of jelly, originally and properly made from quinces. Quiddanet (1616): "a sweet mixture thicker than a sirup, and not so thicke nor stiffe as marmalet." Judging by these definitions,* **Quiddany** *seems to be the early name for clear fruit jelly.*

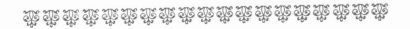

Too Make Gosbery tarts Green
[41]

Make youre Covers of shuger past,
butt Lett the past bee pritey stife,
then Lay the bottom of the cover with suger
and Lay a Row of gusberys as Close as you Can,
then stow more suger,
and then Lay another Row of gosberys,
then lay the top thick with suger,
and put one a Led [lid] one youre tart, cut in holes
that the heat of the oven may com to the gosberyes
youre tarte must bee shallow and thin and
you cant put less then a pound of suger in a
Resonable tart
the oven must bee heat very well not to
burne or scortch,
as sone as the tarts ar in
the suger and the gosberys will boyle, as in a skillett,
when the gosberys Looks Clere, take them out,
thay are enough—

Too Presarve Peard plums

[42]

Take youre pere plums and way them
and putt a pound of suger to a pound of them
then take youre plums and
picke them with a gret nedell
and as you pricke them Lay them in [sugar],
the suger must bee fine beaten,
take a Litell water
and sprinkel one them too Desolve youre suger,
it must not bee above 8 or 9 spunfuls,
sett them one a few embers to desolve
and when thay are desolved
sett them by for an houer or 2:
Then you must boyle them up as fast as you Can
Keep priking of them as thay boyle and
skim them well
take Care you not over boyle them,
thay need not so much boyling
as any other sweet metts,
thay will jelly with keeping,
when thay are boyled
Lett them stand till thay are Cold
before you put them in youre glases —

Too Presarve Gosberys

[43]

Take youre gusberys and stone them,
if you will have them Look white,
you must take them when thay are Ripe,
and to a pound of gusberys a pound of suger,
wett with gelley of green gosberys
then boyle suger to a Candy hith,
then Cole it
and put in youre gosberys and boyle them up quick
you must put them out in glasses —

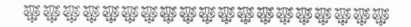

Too make Paste of Pipins green at St Johns but after thay will not

[44]

Take sum green pipens and pare them,
very thin only the out side that is green,
and to a pound of youre pipins a pound of suger
boyled to Candy hight
then put youre pulpe in to it,
and boyle it till it Com Clere of the bottam
of the skillett,
then lay it out for youre use,
you may put sum muske and a Littell Rose watter—

St. Johns Day. *The title means that pippins picked and preserved before St. Johns Day will make green paste, but later ones will not. St. Johns Day, June 24th, the traditional date celebrated throughout Europe as Midsummer, a day of festivity from remotest pagan times, it became the day celebrated as the birthday of John the Baptist, six months before Christmas.*

Too make syrup of vilets

[45]

Take youre violets, and pick them very Clene
then put them in a peutor pott, with water
and sett them by the fire with a few
embers under and a bout the pot
till thay bee enough,
then you must strain them out,
and to 1/2 a pint of juce you putt
a pound and a 1/2 of suger,
put them together and Lett them stand one night,
and then you must heate sum water in A pot,
and sett a silver bason with the surrup in it over the
pot of water, too Desolve the sugger,
and when it is Desolved you must keep it scumed
and when it is Cold put it in to a glass—

Too Make Oring Marmolett
[68]

Take a pound of Apells pared and grated
then put them into a skillet of water
a pound of shuger well beaten,
when it is all most boyled
put 4 oz of oring pele finly minsed,
and the juce of 2 or 3 oringes,
then boyle it too a marmolet,
youre oringes must bee Cutt in halfes and
pared Very thin,
and watered 2 or 3 days and boyled in 3 or 4 waters,
till thay bee tender then mince them and use them —

Too make Jumbals of Apricocks
[71]

Take Apricocks
stone them and
slice them into a dish,
and sett the Dish over the fire
and stur them and breke them,
till thay bee so dry till thay will not stick to the dish,
nor youre fingers,
then make them up in to Roles as smal as a Rush,
with fine suger,
so make them up into fine knots,
so dry them in a stov, and keep them in a Drye
place for youre use

Jumbals *(1678), "a sort of sugared paste, wreathed into knots."*
Stove, stov, stow, *a hot air bath or a heated box for same (old
English). Among confectioners (1706) "it is a little closet well stopt
on all sides . . . several rows of shelves, one above another, made
of wires, to hold the sweet meats that are to be dried."*

Too Dry Churrys:

[72]

Take too a pound a Churys the 3d part of a
pound of suger,
you may stone them if yu plese
then sett them one a quick fire,
and Lett them more then 1/2 presarve,
as you doe other Churyes
then Lett them Ly in a syrup a day
then put them into a glass, or earthen Culender,
and strain all the moysture from them,
so put them in too Dishes to dry
Lett them not toutch one another
Sett them into an oven or stov to dry turning
them oftenn —

Too Dry Churrys or Apricocks

[76]

Take one pound of Lofe suger
and wett it into a syrup,
then boyle it till it bee prity thick,
then put in 4 lb of Churrys, stoned
and heat them throuly but not boyle them at all,
then Lay them out and dry them in the sunn,
the Apricocks must be scalded and then heated twise
before thay bee Laid out —

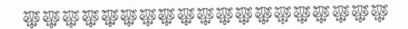

Armeniaca malus major.
The greater Ap{}̈̈ecocke tree.

Too Dry Apricocks or Plums

[77]

Take the Apricocks and stone them and pare them,
then take 1/2 the waight in suger finely betten,
then take the better 1/2 of the suger
strew it upon the Apricocks, being put into a
silver bason,
and Lett them stand till the suger bee wetted,
then sett them over the fire and
Lett them boyle till thay bee tender and Cleare
and as thay boyle Cast over them the rest
of the suger,
and presently take it of the fire before
it boyle againe,
and Lett them stand the next
then beat them and take them out of the syrup
and Lay them one Dishes or glases,
seartch sum fine suger over them,
and so sett them one a Cuberd to Drye —

Too Dry Churys or ApryCocks —

[78]

Take to every pound of suger tenn pound of Churys,
beat the suger and strew a Lain of it at the
bottom of the pan,
then stone the Churrys, and put in a Laine of them
& so till all bee don,
then Lett them stand a night
and the next morning put them in a skillit and
boyle them
shakeing them that thay burne not,
when all are boyled put them into a bason againe
and Lett them stand 4 days
then take them out and flat them and turne them
upon a knife
and Dry them if you Can one a stove else in an oven
when dry enough put them in glases for youre use —

Too make marmalett of oring Roots
[81]

Take a pound of oring Roots,
the youngest you can gett,
boyle them tender
blantch them tender to take out the pith,
beat them in a stone mortor
with a qr of a pound of Allmons blanched,
the pap of a Roten pipen,
when it is very fin
take as much of refined suger as the waight of
the pullpe,
boyle it to a Candy hight with as much rose water
as will melt the suger
put in the pulpe and boyle it, allwais sturing of it,
till it Coms Close of the botom of the skillet,
then put it into youre glases for youre use—

Too Make a Grape Creme White
[90]

Take a good quantaty of white graps,
ston them and peel them
put them into a pint of pipen water,
take to them 3/4 of a pound of fine suger,
boyle them till youre grape and youre syrup bee
prity thick,
then Lett it stand till thay bee Cold,
and then seson it too youre tast,
mingle it well together
but Doe not brake youre graps —

Too keepe Churys halfe a yeare too make tarts
[101]

Take 18 of Churys the Last that are ripe
and Lett them bee blood ripe,
slise them in thin peces in a presarving pan Lose
of the Juce
then beat them,
[take] 4 pound of dry pouder suger that ther bee
no Lumps in it,
and strew into the pann as you put youre Churys
then boyle them till your Churys bee very tender
and youre syrup bee thick
then put them into gally pots
and sett them where thay may bee kept dry,
and this you may put into Coffers of past for tarts
and thay will bee very sweed and plesant with out
more suger —
Let the Cofer of the tart bee hardened in the oven
before you putt youre Churys in
and Lett not youre Churys Com in the oven at all —

Gally pot, gallipot, (*pottery brought in galleys, i.e., imported from the Mediterranean*), *a small earthen glazed pot, especially one used by apothecaries for ointment and medicines. Quotations from 1465. 1880: Antrim, "gaily pot, a jam pot."*

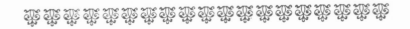

Candy
The glases [glace] for oringes or Angillico or any thing that Lyes in a syrup before you candy them—
[103]

Bee for you Candy them give them a boyle in
there syrup thay Ly in,
then take them out and Lay them upon Ridels
Lett it Lye
then take a pound of suger and a pint of water
boyle till you Desarne [discern] it thicken when you
Rubb it against the panne with the backe side of a
spoune,
then put in youre pitts, or what you Intend to doe,
Rubing it till it begin to grow thick
then make hast and take them out opon a Ridell
for if the Candy bee too thick it will make them white
if you find it doe not drye,
put them into a Cole [cool?] stove
and thay will sone Drye—

Angelica, *an aromatic plant cultivated since 1568 in England for culinary or medicinal purposes and for preparing a confection called "candied Angelica"; cultivated for large ribs of its leaves cut in June to make a candied preserve; also candied Angelica root.*
Riddle, *a utensil formed of strong wires crossing each other at right angles, usually a coarse sieve with a circular wooden rim.*
Riddle wall, *a wall made up with split sticks worked across each other, so* **riddle** *here may be a drying rack of woven withes.*

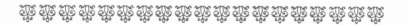

Angellica. Angelica.

Clere Cakes of Angilleco

[104]

Take youre Angilico
boyle it tender,
pele it and grene it, and Cutt it prity small,
but not so small as for past,
then have sum strong Apell water and Juce of Lemon
and mix them as you Like,
dont make it to thick
of the Angellico to a pint take a pound of suger
boyle it to a Candy highth,
and Doe them as other Clere Cakes—

The other is Ancelico with the glased Candy
Cut the youngest stalks a bout 1/2 a yr Longe
sum Longer and sum shorter as you fancy
boyle them but not to tender
pele them and green them and boyle them
to a thin syrup,
and Lett them Lye in it,
and when you have a mind too Candy it,
then open them with a square of wood when you
take them out of the Candy befor mentioned
so stick them one any thing turning them a Litell
for fere thay sticke—

Too make oring tarts
[112]

Take oringes, pare them not too thin
Lay them in watter 2 days
shifting them often in a day,
for 2 days and one night, Civell orenges
so boyle them in a suger and Lay them in paty pans
making the Crust of puff past,
sprinkell suger on every Row,
Laying not too much watter, but as thay presarve them,
for the syrup that is Left you may put it in the pyes
and use Less suger—

Paty pans, *from the French* **pâté,** *a pastry, i.e. pastry baked in a small pan.*

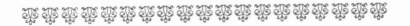

[*Fruit Paste*]

[113]

Take gusberys or plums or Corrants and
putt them in a pitcher,
and boyle them in a pot of watter,
and when thay are tender
squese them through a pece of Canvic [canvas],
then take the waite of the pulpe in dubell
Refined sugger, being beat
and putt to it as much watter,
as much as will melt the suger,
and boyle it up to a thin pulpe in the plate
and sett it over the fire till the suger bee melted —
then put in one paine of glase
and Lett it Run very thin,
then sett it into youre stow till it is hardened
Raise it with youre knife
so put it in to youre stove till it is through Drye —

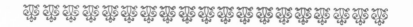

Too presarve Churrys Rasburys Corantes or whit graps
[122]

Stone all butt the Churrys
Take a pound of Churrys, and a pound of suger—
then dip the suger in watter
and put them in a skillet
then boyle them up a pase and then pot them—

How to presarve Mussell plumbs pare plums Damsons or any Red plum
[123]

Take one pound of suger
and dip 3 quarters in watter,
so Lett it stand and melt,
then quodell [coddle] the plums softly one
a slow fire,
then you must doe them thrise,
then put in the Rest of the suger to them and
boyle them up,
but you must not putt the surrup to them till
it is Cold,
and then the surrip will stand upon youre nail
then it is enough
you must doe so with all the Rest—

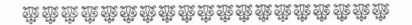

Too Presarve White Bullis
[124]

Take one pound of bullis and quodell them
in water,
and put in a spunfull of suger,
then put them in a sierce [sieve] to drain,
then boyle up a pound of suger and put the white
bullace to them,
and boyle them up a pace,
then pot them,
but you must not put the sirup to them till
thay bee Cold—

Bullace, bullis, *a wild plum, larger than the sloe, two varieties,*
black and white.

Too presarve Apricocks
[125]

Take one pound of Apricocks and stone them and
pare them,
then take one pound of Duble refined sugger and
beat it very small
then take a spunfull of watter in a skillet or
sillver bason,
and put sum of the suger in
then Lay the Aprycocks and Cover them with the
rest of the sugger
and Lett them stand an houer
then put them one the fire and quodell them,
then Lett them stand 2 days
then boyle them up a pace and then pott them,
but you must not putt the surrup too them till
it is Cold —

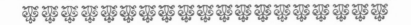

Too Presarve Barberys

[126]

Take one pound of barberys,
and give them twise the wait in suger,
then stone the barberys,
then take a dish and Lay a Layer of suger and a
Layer of barbarys,
then you must take sum barberys and
steep them and
boyl them in sum watter,
then strain them through a search,
and put the pulpe up one them,
and so sett them a side,
and if you doe not like them Raw
then boyle them up a pace and pot them—

A Receipt out of Jane Bullocks Book by M: Pig, to make oring Caks

Take oringes: rost them
Cut them in peces halfes
way them,
take all the meat out
put the Rines in water
boyle them till thay are very tender
Lay them into a dry Cloath to suck out the watter
when thay are prity dry take them out to shred them
pound them in a mortor till thay are small,
have Redy as much suger as oringes finly beaten
and sifted
take one halfe of the suger, and the past
of the orenges,
and sett it one [a] soft fire,
stur it very well but besure it doe not boyle nor simer
then add the other part of the suger,
and the juce of the oringes with Curnils and skins
peiled out Clene,
Lett it stand over the fire a 1/4 of an houer to Clere
Lett it not boyle besure,
Drop it one peces of Cloath
and putt it up in a warme stow,
next day turn them and Lay so together 2 or 3 days,
turning once a day thay will bee dry enough —

Too Candie flouers
[134]

Take gum araback steep it in rose water
till it bee desolved,
then take a Littell suger Candy
bruse it small like spoiles of sinomon,
then take the flouers in the heat of the day:
wett them over with the gum arobeck
and strew suger Candy one it over them,
and Lay or stick them on the bottom of a sife [sieve]
then with a fether wett them
and Lay them in the sunn to dry—

what fruit soever you presarve
put in a Littell Apell watter,
it will make it of an oring Culer
and make the fruit keep better from molding
and will Continew all the yeare,
it is only the Liquor of boyled Apells—

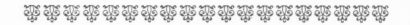

Too make past of Aprycocks or white plums

[135]

pare and stone them,
quarter them
put them in a dish and strew as much suger
on them,
Cover them Close and Lett it stand all night,
bruse them with a back of a spone,
then boyle it in its one Liquor
till it bee as thick as past,
then dry it,
it will bee as clere as amber—

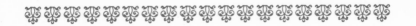

Too Presarve Pipins green

[137]

Take small green pipins
pick off the black ends
prick hols throu them,
Codell them prity tender
pele them
then put them in too Clarifyed suger
being warmed
then sett them over the fier the span of 2 houers
Close Covered
then take them off and scum them,
when thay are Cold put away the suger from them
and put fresh suger too them,
then sett twise or 3 tims Close Covered over the fire,
Lett them boyle 3 or 4 walops but not to fast,
then scum them and when thay are Cold
putt them up in potts—

Wallop (*cookery*), *to boil violently with a noisy bubbling. Also to beat soundly.*

Too make gosbery Marmalett

[138]

put the gosberys in a pot or mugg
and sett them one boyling watter
Lett the fruit bee very soft
then put them in a Coulender, and
Lett the Liquor & substance Run from them,
then take 3 or 4 of youre grenest Apells,
pare and Cutt them in thin slices and
strain them too the gosberys past
then take as much suger as the pap doth way and
boyle it to a Candy Hight —

For a Cold or Cough being a thin rume

[140]

Take a pound of Resons of the sonn,
wash and stone them,
boyle them in a quart or more of Clarett wine
till thay pulpe
then strain the wine from them and
put in 1/2 the waight of the pulpe, of suger candy,
and boyle it till it bee Like marmolett,
put it up in potts and use sum now and then —

Too presarve gren Wallnuts
[142]

Take the first green Wallnuts
when a needle will Run through them,
cut off the stalkes and the peest,
then prick them a full of hols with a needell
then have them Redy two watters,
put them in the first,
make them booth boyle as fast as you Cann
a Littell while in the first,
then shift them a while till thay are tender,
then take them of and peele them
having 2 boyling watters Redy
Lett them have a Walop or tow in eatch watter,
then take them up and dry them in a Cloath
then way them, and take the waight in suger
to a pound of sugger, a pint of watter
then Lett the water and suger boyle and
scum it well,
then putt the walnuts in,
and Lett them boyle about 1/2 an houer
Rather more then Less
then take it of the fire and sett it by all night,
next day heat it againe scalding hot,
then take up the walnuts and Lay them even—
then boyle the fyrst up a pace till its prity thick:
and scum it very well,
then pore it in the pots
next day paper them—

⟦ CHEESE ⟧

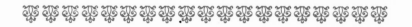

Too make fresh Chees new
[64]

Take a quart of new milke and sett it one the fire
when it boyles poure in a quart of the
souerest Creme you Can gett,
then Cover it and Lett it stand one the fire
untill it begin to Curde, or gather
then whay it in a strainer
when it is well Whayd forse the Curd through
a strainer,
then sesen it with suger and Rose watter,
and put it into a Littel Culender,
if you kepe it one night it will bee the better for you,
doe not put it to the Creme untill you eate it—

Too Make Chees Cakes
[70]

Take New milke from the [cow],
then put in a pint of new Creme, sweet,
then put in a Litel Rennet to make it Cum
then Lett it stand one houre
and gather youre Curd as you doe a Cheese,

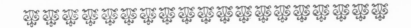

and take up the Curd and put it into a
Course strainer,
a Litell at a time, but doe not Crush them
but Lett the whay drop from them Clene
then take a pint of boyled Creme with larg mace in it
then Lett it stand till it bee Cold
and before the Creme boyle put in
9 yeollks of eggs beaten with a Littell milke,
then give one wallup of the fire, with the Creme,
then take 3/4 of a pound of Corants,
and plumpe them in a Litell water, then warm
then dry them in a cloath, but not bruse them,
then take youre Curd and bruse them in a Mortor
with a pound of butter
till thay are alemost as smouth as boyled Creme,
beat them as thay Com out of the strainer
then put in a hole grated nutmeg,
and as much suger as will sweeten it,
then put in youre Crem and Rose water,
then beat them alltogether in a pan with a nooden, . .
then when thay are Redy to put into the Coffen,
stur in the Corants
first harden the Coffens in the oven then fill them,
and when thay begin to Culler, take them out,
heat youre oven as for manchets, add sum manchets
finly beaten —

Nooden, *not found in any dictionary consulted but probably it means*
a wooden stick or a wooden spoon.
Nood, *a wood (Somerset).*

Too make slipping Cheese

[80]

Take new milke and sum Creme
and sum warme water, as much as will just warme it
Like milke
then put in as much quick renen in it as will
make it Com
Cover it till it Coms then breke it
and when you have dun put in 2 or 3 Dishfulls of
Cold wator —
as you Lay the Curd in to the fatt [vat] pour still
Cold water
to Cold the Curd and make it tender
when you have laid out all the Curd,
press it very hard with your hand
still pouring on Cold water
then turn your Chees one youre shuter,
then put the Chees and sheter into a bole of
Cold water
so Lett it Ly 3 or 4 houers in the watter,
then putt it into the fatt [vat] and turn it
every houer
for 2 or 3 houers to gether
Lett a fresh Cloath bee put too it,
wett them in Cold water
Lett them stand all day in the press
take it out at night and put sum salt one it
and sett it in the press for an houer,
then take biter Docke Leves and Lay them under

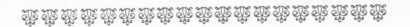

and upon it,
Lett them Ly too Days then Cutt it—

Shooter, shuter, sheter, *a board placed between cheeses under a press. Shuttleworths account (1586) mentions five cheese vats and one shewter.*

Too Make Chees Cake with out Curd

[86]

Take a quart of Creme and boyle it with sum mace,
slising as many oring roots as will make it very thick,
keep it besure from burning
then, when it is Cold
take a Quarter of a pound of sweet butter,
well beaten with Rose water
knede youre butter with roots,
then take 6 egs all the yeolks
and a peneworth of manchets grated
a 1/4 of a pound of Corants when thay
are plumped,
one nutmeg slised thin—
Too make the Crust take a pound of flouer,
1/2 a pound of butter beaten with rose water,
put a prity Quantaty of suger
2 egs one white
sum 4 spunfulls of Cold watter
then bake them in a quick oven, but not to hott—

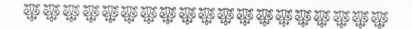

Too make Chees Cake

[93]

Take 15 quarts of new milk warme as it is
from the Cow, or else make it so warm
then, putt too it 4 spunfulls of Rennett,
and Lett it stand,
while it is Coming, make youre Cofins
too 2 pound of flouer,
take 1/2 a pound of butter
youre Liquor must boyle and then youre Chees is
pritiwell Com,
then put it in a Chese Cloath and Lett it
hang and Drain
till all the whay bee kum from it,
then take the Curd and Rubb it through a sciefe of
haire and with thy hand,
too this Curd take 2 pounds Corants
one pound of suger
3 great nutmegs,
6 spunfuls of Rose water
the yeolk of 20 eggs,
one pound of buter
a quart of Creme,
and mix all these with the Curd,
and well breke the butter,
and Lett the Coffin bee hardened in the oven
and then fill them not to full
and Lett the oven bee quick
and 1/2 an houer will bake them

⟨ MISCELLANEOUS ⟩

Too Lay Samphire

[47]

Take youre samphire and wash it
and lay it in vineger 4 days
and the 5th day boyle it
but Lett youre water boyle beefore you put it in
then keep it Covered till it bee soft,
take it of
and keep it Close Covered till it bee close [cool?]
then take it out to a pot or barell,
and strow a handful of sallt into it,
not too much for it will make it black —
fill youre vesell with veniger, as much as will
Cover it —

Samphire, *the plant* Crithmum maritimum (*growing on rocks by the sea*), *the aromatic, saline, fleshy leaves of which are used in pickles.*

Too Make a tart of spinaige

[67]

Take a good Dele of spinaige and boyle it in water
and a Littell salt, and when it is boyled well
Drain out the water very Clene,
take the yeolks of eggs and Creme
strain them with the spinaige through a strainer,
and seson it with suger,
put too it a slise of butter
then put them in the Coffen
and boyle them—

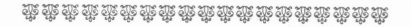

Too Make Cabidg Poridg *without* *flesh*

[89]

Take youre Cabidg and pick them Clene
and put them in to a pot of watter,
and Lett it boyle so an houer,
then putt into it a pound of butter or more
According too youre quantaty
putt in Cloves mace peper and salt,
boyle all these together till it bee all mash,
then put slices of bred into it,
youre bred must bee put at bottam of the dish
then take youre Cabidg and Lay it one youre sipets
with sum Littell of youre Liquor,
then take 6 eggs with yelks only,
and beat them with warme Creme
pour it one the Cabidg
and sarve it up—

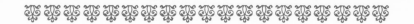

Too make red Culer

[132]

take Cuchinele a 1/4 of an oz
beat it very fine
1/2 an oz of roach [rock] allum,
1/2 a pound of Churfeild suger
and 1/4 of a pound of water
boyle and strain it throu a Cloath,
you may Culer as high or as pale as you plese —

Another way too Couler

[133]

Take Cuochanele
bruse it small
Lay it in water over night
strain it through a fine Cloath
so you may Couler anything pink or scarlett —

Too make oyle of St. Johns wort
[141]

Take good store of the buds of St. Johns wort
and put them into the best oyle you can gett
sett it in the sunn Covered from dust and flies
till it Look very red with the flouers —

Too Pickell Larg Coucumbrs
[144]

Take Larg green Coucumbers wipe them Clene
and take a splinter out of them
then with the end of a spoune scrape out the seeds
then put Cloves mace peper hole horse Radish
scraped Cloufe of shallote or garlecke and
mustard seed
put the splinter into its place
and ty the Coucumber Round with a thred
very Close,
and put them as Close as you Can
into a deepe erthen pott well glased,
then take good white wine vinegar

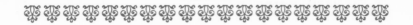

and putt into it of the same Ingrediences
you putt into the Cowcumbers
a Littell of every one with salt too youre tast,
and 2 or 3 bay Leves
Lett all boyle together,
and pour it boyling on the Cowcumbers
Cover them up Close
after 3 or 4 days boyle the pickell again
pouring it hot up on them
this doe 3 or 4 times at 2 or 3 days Distance
and keep them Close Covered
and thay will keep the hole yeare —

Here ends the book of Coockarys In great hast
trancscrided by Edward Blackfan
the 25th of October 1702

Shallot, *a small onion cultivated for use in flavoring salads, etc.*

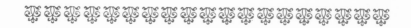

Doctor Wickliff in the buty of providence —

There is a secret providence which over Rules
all these worldly events in such a manner as is not
Accountable to human Reson
even amongst secular business
which wee are Apt to thinke within our Retch
and Compass —
There is nothing so much under the power of the
wisest Counsels Indevors
but the providence of god may Interpose
for the disspoynting of it
and render it Ineffectual —

[The above message is present among the recipes, being located
below recipe #82, "To Ice a great Cake the Wood street way."]

APPENDIX

Index to Recipes

BEVERAGES

BAKED GOODS

CUSTARDS & PUDDINGS

PRESERVES, JELLY, & CANDY

CHEESE & CHEESE CAKE

MISCELLANEOUS

Index of Herbs, Seasoning, & Condiments

Index of Utensils

Index of Proper Names & Places

Index of Words Defined

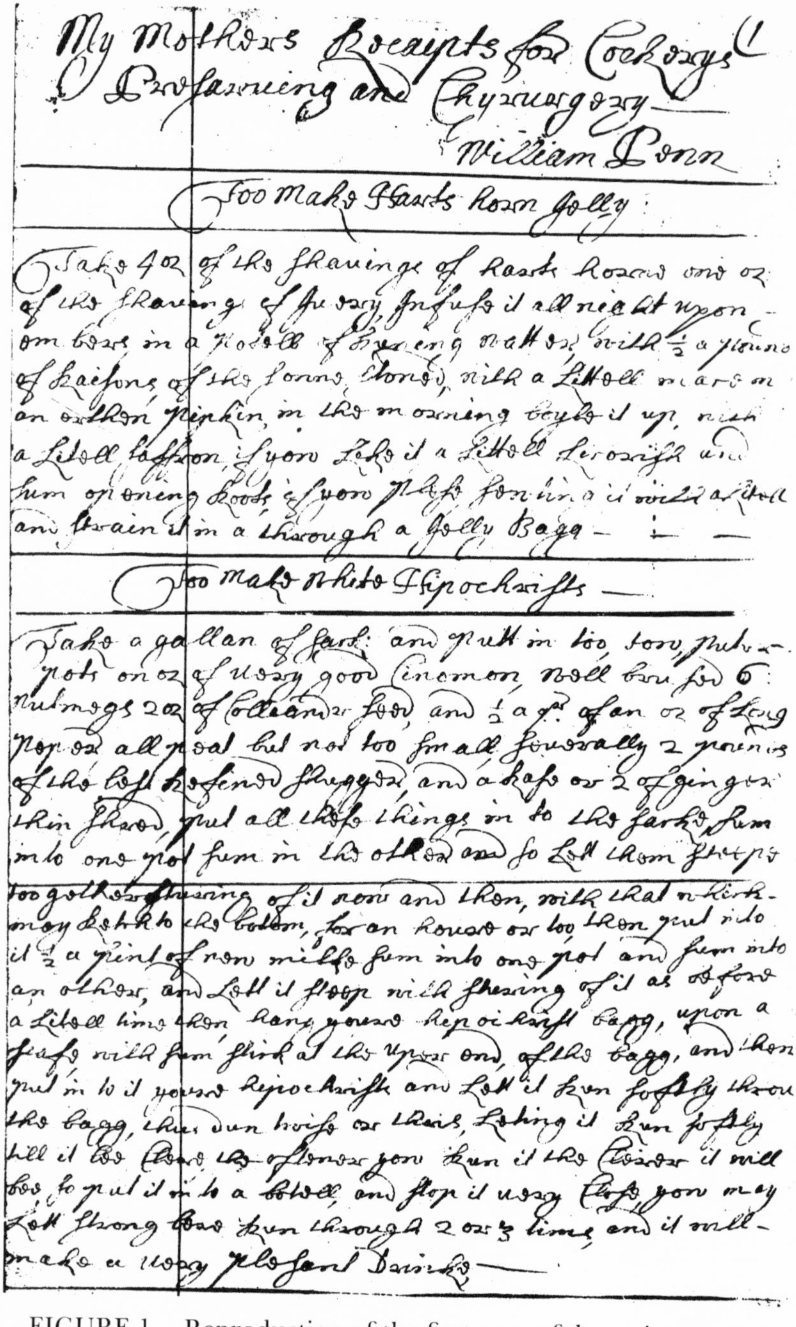

My Mothers Recaipts for Cookerys
Presarveing and Chyrurgery
William Penn

Too Make Harts horn Jelly

Take 4 oz of the shavinge of harts horne one oz of the shaveing of Ivery infuse it all night upon embers in a pottle of spring watter with ½ a pound of Raisons of the sonne stoned with a Littell mace in an erthen pipkin in the morning boyle it up with a Litell saffron if you Like it a Littell strongish an[d] hum opening roots if you please ... it with a Littell and strain it in a through a Jelly Bagg — : —

Too Make white Hipochrists

Take a gallan of sack and putt in too, tow, pulve- pots on oz of very good Cinemon well brused 6 nutmegs 2 oz of Colleander seed and ½ a qr of an oz of Long pepper all beat but not too small severally 2 pounds of the best refined shuggar and a race or 2 of ginger thin sliced put all these things in to the sacke then into one pot then in the other and so Lett them steepe together stiring of it now and then, with that which may settle to the bottom, for an houre or too then put into it ½ a pint of new milke then into one pot and then into an other, and Lett it steep with stiring of it as before a Litell time then hang youre hepocrist bagg, upon a peece with then stick at the upper end of the bagg, and then put in to it youre hipocrist and Lett it run softly throu the bagg, then run twise or thrise, Letting it run softly till it bee cleare the oftener you run it the clearer it will bee, so put it in to a bottell and stop it very close you may Lett strong beare run through 2 or 3 time and it will make a very plesant drinke —

FIGURE 1. Reproduction of the first page of the recipe manuscript, headed "My Mothers Recaipts for Cookerys Presarving and Chyrurgery – William Penn."

Too Make a Parsnep Puding 46

Take them Parsneps and boyle them till they be very soft, then mash them very small and pick out the hard seeds, then put to it some grated bread or flowre, and a good many Currants, some nutmage and a little sugar, and when you have mixed them together put too an indeferent quantity the yolkes of 4 or 5 eggs: mett it with Crome till it bee as thin as batter, and then fry them quick if you will boyle it you must not make it so thin and boyle it in a Cloth spread with butter, when it is boyled melt some butter with sack and sugar for the sam

Too Lay Samp Hire

Take your Samphire and wash it, and Lay it in Uineger 4 daye and the 5th Day: boyle it but as your water boyle before you put it in then keep it covered till it bee soft, take it of and keep it close covered till it bee close, then take it out to a pot or barell, and throw a handfull of salt into it not too much for it will make it blacke fill your vessell with Uineger, as much as will cover it —

Too Make French Bred —

Take ½ a bushell of mele if it bee good, also yeast a pawngerfull, mett it with warme water, but not boyled knead it not too stiff sett it by the fire 2 or 3 howers, covered with a cloath then meold it in to Loves, and Lett it stand till it bee ouer toe hott mash it with the yolke of an egg, and a spoonfull, or 2 of bear, Lett it stand an hower and a halfe —

FIGURE 2. Page 16 of the recipe manuscript, containing recipes #46 "Too Make a Parsnep Puding," #47 "Too Lay Samphire," #48 "Too Make French Bred."

169

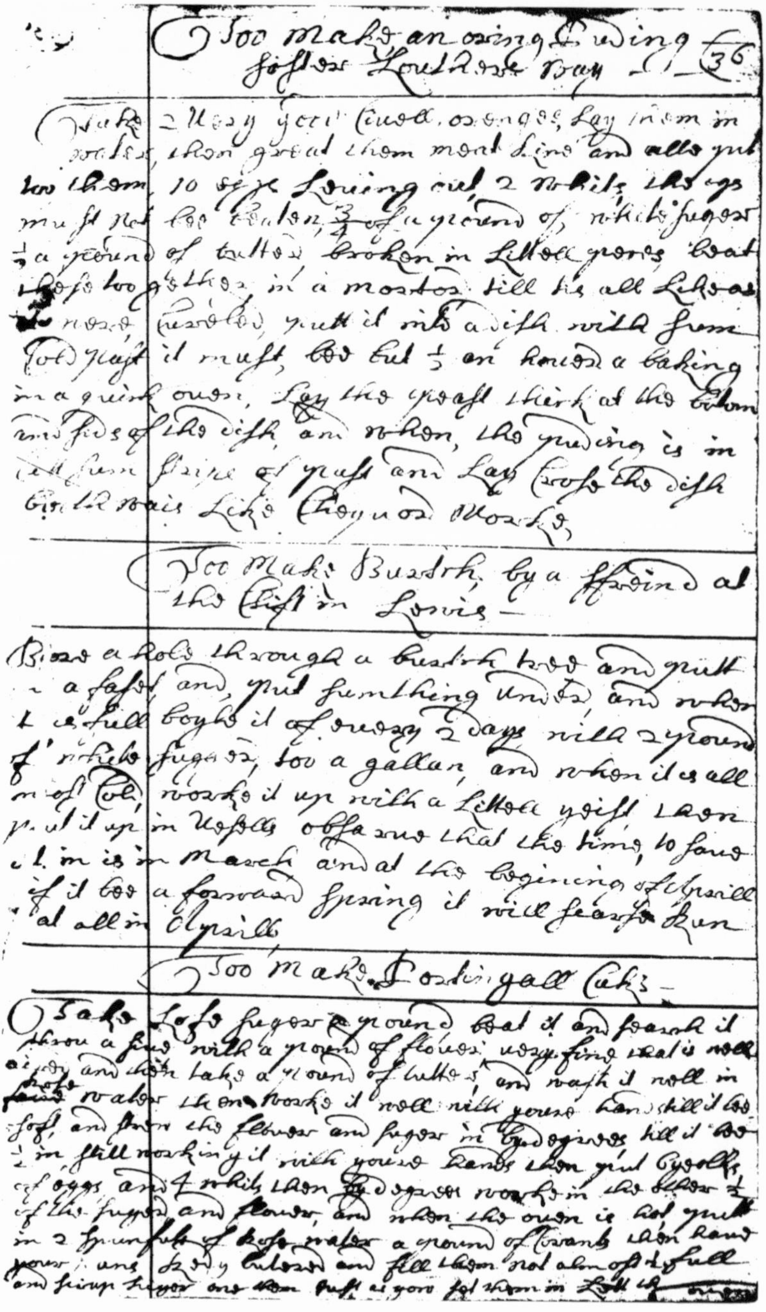
Too Make an oring Puding Sister Louthers way 36

Too Make Burtch, by a Friend at the Clift in Lewis

Too Make Portingall Cake

FIGURE 3. Page 36 of the recipe manuscript, containing recipes #98 "Too Make an oring Puding Sister Louthers way," #99 "Too Make Burtch, by a Friend at the Clift in Lewis," #100 "Too Make Portingall Cake."

(57)   Too Pickell Larg Cocumbrs

Take Larg green Cocumbers wipe them Cleen
and take a splinter out of them then with the
end of a spoone scrape out the seeds then pull Cloves
mace nepe or hole horse reddish scraped clouse of
shollot or garlicke and mustad seed put the splinter
into it place and ty the Cocumber round with a
threed tirey tite and pull them as close as you Can
in to a deepe earthen pott well glased, then take
good white wine vinegar and pull into it of the
of the same Ingrediences you pull into the ———
Cocumbers, a Litell of every one with salt
too your taste, and 2 or 3 bay Leves Let all boyle
together and powre it boyling on the Cocumbers
Cover them up close after 3 or 4 days boyle the
pirkell again powering it hot upon them
this doe 3 or 4 times at 2 or 3 days Distance and
keep them close Covered, and they will keep
the hole yeare ———

Here ends the book of Cookary
In great hast transcribed by ———

Edward Blackfan

the 25 of october 1702

FIGURE 4. Last page of the recipe manuscript, containing
recipe #144 "Too Pickell Larg Cocumbrs," and the signature
of the transcriber, Edward Blackfan, under the parting note,
"Here ends the book of Cookary In great hast transcrided,"
with the date 25 October 1702.

This portrait of Guli Penn's mother, Lady Mary Proude Springett (1625–1682), is on display at Pennsbury Manor, near Philadelphia. *Courtesy Pennsylvania Historical & Museum Commission.*

AN ACCOUNT OF

THE LIFE OF

GULIELMA MARIA SPRINGETT PENN 1644–1694

by Evelyn Abraham Benson

GEORGE SHUMWAY, *Publisher*

York, Pennsylvania

Contents

Prologue

Remember thou wast the love of my youth, and much the joy of my life—the most beloved as well as the most worthy of all my earthly comforts; and the reason of that love was more thy inward than thy outward excellencies, which yet were many. God knows and thou knowest I can say it was a match of his making; and God's image in us both was the first thing, and the most amiable and engaging ornament in our eyes. Now I am to leave thee, and that without knowing whether I shall ever see thee more in this world. Take my counsel into thy bosom, and let it dwell with thee in my stead while thou livest.

So wrote William Penn to his beloved wife, Gulielma Maria Springett Penn as he prepared to sail for Pennsylvania in August, 1682.[1]

Two years later in Philadelphia, facing the perils of a voyage back to England, knowing well that many a traveler never returns, William Penn made his will and wrote with it a farewell letter to accompany the will:[2]

My most dear G. Penn
Being now to leave this part of the world, & ready to come to thee, not knowing how the Lord pleaseth to deal with me in my passage, lest the sea be my grave, & the deeps my sepulchre, I write unto thee, my beloved one, the true & great Joy & Crown of my life above all visible Comforts, allways vallued by me, & honored above women . . . praying the god of our many & rich blessings to be with you . . .
I should think well of thy coming & living here where a sweet place & retired is provided for thee & thyn, this being the place god by his Providence has given to me & my offspring and where is a fine people . . .
live spareing, have little cumber teach the children love & humility to the people & that my promises to them be in all fullfilled . . . Know this, that tis for thy childrens good thou comest, & by thy sweet, grave & upright carriage & life among them thou introducest the children . . . into those capacitys they are like to have in the land . . . farewell my dearest & my love

yours in the best of love
as god would have it
Wm Penn

Philadelphia
6th 6 mo [August] 1684

Happily William Penn made a speedy voyage home. On October 6 his ship obligingly anchored off the Sussex coast so that he came ashore "within seven miles of my house," a distance quickly covered by an agile horseman eager to see his own.[3]

Gulielma's Parents, Sir William and Lady Mary Springett

There is an old saying, the more things change, the more they are the same. So it is that the gifted youth of every generation, from our own day back through the vistas of history, often seem to revolt from the standards, values and aspirations of their elders, to raise a new banner in a new cause. The parents of Gulielma Springett were born into an age of idealistic revolt as great as any that came before or after them.

In the days of Elizabeth, England became wealthy by trade and pillage; luxury and vice burgeoned. Yet with wealth, both culture and learning flourished; Elizabeth had the Bible translated into Welsh; her successor sponsored its translation into English.

For the first time in England, as in continental Europe, printing presses turned out thousands of copies of the Bible in the language of the people. For the first time all could read this tremendously stimulating book—and they did. Sons of poverty and sons of wealth read it and many sorrowed at the wide discrepancies between the simplicity of early Christians, the ideals of the Sermon on the Mount, and the rough, rowdy, licentious and luxurious world in which they lived. They questioned any established church which controlled great wealth but failed to transfer Christ's message from the Bible to living action. They noted that Christ had never advocated prison, torture and execution for those who differed with him. They observed that the official churches, in their ceremonies and activities, had departed from the original Word of God, and they were convinced that the true way could be found by individual Christians searching the scriptures.

The parents of both William Penn and Gulielma Springett were born into this questioning and robust world of seventeenth century England. William Penn's father, son of a sea captain, became admiral of the English fleet at the age of twenty-seven; the father of Gulielma Springett died a colonel in the Parliamentary army at the age of twenty-three. Admiral Penn's worldly ambitions came into violent conflict with the Bible studies of his serious son, but Gulielma Springett's parents, from earliest youth, were concerned in efforts to understand the Word.

Guli's mother, Mary Proude, was an orphan heiress at the age of three years, brought up in the household of her guardian, Sir Edward Partridge, whose widowed sister, Madam Katherine Springett, lived on the Partridge estate with her three small children. These children were Mary Proude's playmates; she especially admired the manly little William Springett.

Madam Springett sympathized with those who criticized the over-worldly church. She sent William to Cambridge, as being more sober than Oxford. He matriculated at St. Catharine's College. There he had a Puritan tutor, a protégé of his mother's.

At Cambridge and Oxford in 1640 it was both daring and dangerous to criticize the established church, so intelligent youth, who love to live dangerously, held many a bull session discussing the worth of religious ceremonies or church doctrine, and the opinions of radical teachers.

After Cambridge, William Springett read law in London at the Inns of Court. His influential uncle and guardian, Sir Thomas Springett, a steady royalist, introduced young William to the court of Charles I. A handsome, athletic, intelligent young man, William Springett's natural gifts and family connections held promise of a bright future in any direction he might choose. He caught the eye of Charles I who knighted him *Sir* William Springett when scarcely more than twenty years old.

Meanwhile, back home in Kent, rebel Mary Proude was developing a mind of her own on religious matters. Some of her ideas came from dissenting sermons which a servant girl read to her on Sunday afternoons. She insisted on walking miles to hear non-conformist preachers. She made it hard for the Partridge family by refusing to kneel when they prayed daily at family worship, and by encouraging the servants in similar rebellious behavior. Her elders warned that she would never find a gentleman to be her husband—only one of the meaner sort would consider her.

But Madam Springett, loving Mary in spite of her contrariness, favored a marriage between her son and this unorthodox young lady. Mary Proude was eighteen when *Sir* William Springett came home from London to marry his childhood playmate. After many long talks pro and con concerning the worth of orthodox ceremonies, they made an unheard of decision—to be married without a ring.

At the baptism of their first child by a non-conformist preacher, William Springett held the child himself, scandalizing his well-placed relatives who might have Puritan leanings, but were certainly not dissenters. For their second child William and Mary decided against infant baptism altogether.

But William Springett did not live to see this second child, Gulielma Maria. The wars between Parliament and Charles I had begun. Sir William took the Scotch Covenant against all popery. He became a colonel of the Parliamentary army, raising a regiment at his own expense to fight the royalist forces, and died at Arundel Castle of a fever after the siege and capture of that place in February 1644. He was twenty-three years old.

His young wife's own account of her harrowing trip through the blackness of night, storm, and flood to his death bed and their passionate farewell would be pure melodrama if not told with the simplicity of sincerity and personal experience. A few weeks later was born Gulielma Maria Springett who became the beloved wife of William Penn.

Guli's Childhood

For the first four years of Guli Springett's life her remarkable grandmother, Madam Katherine Partridge Springett, a woman active in preparing cures of all sorts in physic, surgery and for the eyes, lived with her son's widow and the infant Guli. Then Madam Springett died, but her legacy of cures benefited Guli and her family for another generation.

For ten years after William Springett's death Guli's mother lived in an emotional miasma, spiritually at loose ends, seeking she knew not what, finding no satisfaction in either her social or religious life.

Very soon after her husband's death she and infant Guli,

with Madam Springett, moved to Parliamentary London for safety from the cavalier troops that overran the country-side. In London Guli's restless mother "took no notice of any religion, but minded recreation, as it is called, and went after it into many excesses and vanities—as foolish mirth, carding, dancing, singing and frequenting of music meetings: and made many vain visits at jovial eatings and drinkings . . . I also frequented other places of pleasure where vain people resorted to show themselves, and to see others in like excess of apparel, riding about from place to place in the airy mind. But in the midst of this my heart was constantly sad . . . In this restless, distressed state, I often retired into the country, without any company but my daughter and her maid."[4]

During her young widowhood in London Mary Proude Springett counted among her friends the Ellwood family of Oxfordshire who had also moved to the city for safety during the civil war. Thomas Ellwood, five years older than Guli, later wrote, "this friendship devolving from the parents to the children, I became an early and particular play-fellow to her daughter Gulielma, being admitted as such to ride with her in her little Coach, drawn by her footman about Lincoln's Inn-Fields." Guli was no more than two years old at this time, Thomas but five or six, so small and slight that his parents feared he might be a dwarf.[5]

Guli's mother has much more to say of her unsatisfactory life in London during ten years of widowhood, her deep concern in seeking the truth and her grief at never finding it. In 1654 she married Isaac Penington, another seeker, equally troubled about eternal verities. Their attitude toward the new sect of Quakers or Friends was at first scornful, then attentive. Eventually they were drawn to attend Quaker meetings and there found the solace of soul they had sought. The Ellwood family, and many other old friends who visited them occasionally while they lived near Reading, knew nothing of the Penington's interest in the Friends.

In 1658 the Penington family with Guli Springett moved to the Grange at Chalfont in Buckinghamshire, an estate alloted to Isaac as a wedding present by his father, Sir Isaac Penington, a strong Republican and Presbyterian, former Lord Mayor of London. It was almost exactly at this time that Mary, Isaac Penington, and the fourteen year old Gulielma Springett publicly joined the people whom Isaac says "his

understanding and reason had formerly counted contemptible."
Mary Penington's relatives were horrified; Alderman Sir Isaac
Penington of London wrote harshly to his son. The cost in
material wealth and worldly prestige was high, but the peace
of mind and serenity of soul after long and agitated seeking
more than compensated.

Knowing nothing of this, Thomas Ellwood (now a fairly tall
young man), and his father came to spend a day at the Peningtons' new home. "Very much surprised we were," says
Thomas, "when we found they were become Quakers—a
People we had no Knowledge of, and a Name we had till then
scarcely heard of. So great a Change from a free, debonair,
and courtly sort of Behaviour, which we formerly had found
them in, to so strict a Gravity did not a little disappoint our
Expectations of such a pleasant Visit as we used to have . . .

"For my part I sought the Company of the Daughter [Guli]
whom I found gathering Flowers in the Garden, attended by
her Maid who was also a Quaker. Though she treated me
with a courteous Mien, yet, young as she was, the Gravity of
her Look and Behaviour struck such an Awe upon me, that
I [was] not so much Master of myself as to pursue any further
Converse with her.

"We staid Dinner, which was very handsome, and lacked
nothing to recommend it to me but the want of Mirth and
pleasant Discourse . . . the Weightiness that was upon their
Spirits and Countenances keeping down the Lightness that
would have been up in us."[6]

The Ellwoods returned more than once in 1659 to Chalfont
to seek understanding of a faith which could so wholly absorb
one of Isaac Penington's distinguished background and high
cultural attainments. Once that year when Thomas came alone
he found that Guli had just recovered from small-pox and that
day came downstairs to sit in the parlor for the first time since
her illness, "the Marks of her Distemper fresh upon her."

From the moment the Peningtons publicly avowed their
Quaker faith, Guli's mother tells us, they "endured patiently
despisings, reproaches, cruel mockings, and scornings from
relations, acquaintances and neighbors, those of our own
rank, and those below us, nay, even our own servants. To
every class we were a by-word; they would wag the head at us,
accounting us fools, mad and bewitched . . . Our own tenants
withheld what the law gave, and put us into the Courts of

Chancery because we could not swear. Our relations also taking that advantage, we were put out of our dwelling house in an injurious, unrighteous manner. Thus we were stripped of my husband's estate and a great part of mine."[7] A portrait of Mary Proude Springett Penington done in 1663 by Nicholas Maes shows her a truly formidable woman clad in black silk with large white collar, looking well able to cope with the direst affliction.[8]

Actual eviction from the Grange at Chalfont did not come about until a few years after the loss of title. The erudite Isaac Penington, esteemed of John Milton, henceforth embarked upon a career of Quaker polemics. A gentle person in whom all recognized unusual grace of spirit, he devoted his talents and his scholarly training to speaking and writing of the heavenly gifts to be found in the Quaker faith. Following the Restoration (1660) he was imprisoned six times for periods varying from a month to three years. He made good use of this confinement to increase his literary output.

Isaac Penington's father, Sir Isaac Penington, whose wrath was unbounded at his son's new faith, fell upon even more evil days himself in 1660. He had been one of the judges at the trial of Charles I. Upon the restoration of the Stuart kings in 1660 his estates were confiscated and he died a prisoner in the Tower of London, December 1661.[9]

By 1660 the Quaker spiritual seed had reached the soul of Thomas Ellwood. He gave up all worldly advantages his own family might offer and henceforth cast his lot with the Peningtons, with whom he remained closely associated all his days. Through the influence of Guli Springett's stepfather Isaac Penington, Ellwood became Latin reader to the blind poet, John Milton, in London, for a considerable period, until this delightful interlude was interrupted, first by Ellwood's ill health, and a second time by his arrest for attending a Quaker meeting. Released from prison (1662), Ellwood visited the Peningtons at Chalfont and there remained for seven years as family business manager and tutor to Guli Springett's young Penington brothers.[10]

Guli's Suitors

These were the years of Guli Springett's blooming young womanhood. In spite of the social curse of Quakerism, her hand was sought in marriage by suitors of high degree and title. The beauty of her person and character were, of course, of prime significance, but these gentlemen were not unaware that she was an heiress in her own right, worth ten thousand pounds clear.

Ellwood admitted "sparklings of desire" himself when he described Mary Penington's fair daughter Guli:

"She having now arrived to a marriageable Age, and being in all respects a very desirable Woman (whether respect was had to her outward Person, which wanted nothing to render her completely comely; or to the endowments of her Mind, which were every way extraordinary and highly obliging; or to her outward Fortune, which was fair, and which with some hath not the last, nor the least Place in Consideration) . . . was openly and secretly sought, and solicited by many, and some of them almost of every Rank and Condition: Good and Bad, Rich and Poor, Friend and Foe. To whom, in their respective Turns (till he at length came, for whom she was reserved) she carried herself with so much Evenness of Temper, such courteous Freedom, guarded with the strictest Modesty, that, as it gave Encouragement, or Ground of Hopes to none, so neither did it administer any matter of Offence, or just Cause of Complaint to any . . .

"Neither was I so . . . divested of all Humanity, as not to be sensible of the real and innate Worth and Virtue which adorned that excellent Dame, and attracted the Eyes and Hearts of so many with the greatest Importunity to seek and solicit her; nor was I so devoid of natural Heat as not to feel some Sparklings of Desire as well as others. But the force of Truth, and Sense of Honour, supprest whatever would have risen beyond the Bounds of fair and virtuous Friendship . . .

"Having observed how some others had befool'd themselves by misconstruing her common Kindness (expressed in an innocent, open, free and familiar Conversation, springing from the abundant Affability, Courtesy and Sweetness of her natural Temper) to be the effect of a singular Regard and Affection to them, I resolved to shun the Rock on which I had seen so many run and split . . . I governed myself in a free, yet respectful Carriage towards her that I thereby enjoyed as much of her Favour and Kindness in a virtuous and firm Friendship as was fit for her to shew or for me to seek . . . "

One of Guli's suitors, John Vaughan, Earl of Carberry, whom Pepys refers to as "one of the lewdest fellows of the age," addressed to her a letter (December 8, 1664) calculated to impress a lady of known religious principles:
"Madam
As in Silence and stillnesse wee often obtain better answers of our heavenly father when clamour and Inportunity cannot prevail, so I hope that notwithstanding your Commands put a stop to the importunate part of my Addresses . . . Hee I hope, may have opened for mee a clearer way into your favour . . . than if I had intruded by my own importunity . . . "[11]

Another worldly gentleman of the time who took constant notes on all he heard and saw, wrote down a few words about Guli gleaned from current gossip which, like Ellwood, could report no ill of this "excellent Dame:"

"Her fortune, quality, and good humour gave her the importunity of many suitors of extraordinary condition, e.g. Lord Brookes and Lord John Vaughan, etc.; but valueing the Unity of beliefe and selfe deniall of her profession above the glories of the World, resisted their motions till Providence brought a man of equall condicion and fortune to herself to the syncere embracing of the same Fayth."[12]

Days of Trial

The year of the Great Plague in London, 1665, John Milton asked Ellwood to find him a place in the country away from the contagion. "I took a pretty Box for him in Giles-Chalfont, a Mile from me, of which I gave him Notice, and intended to have waited on him and seen him well settled in it."

But Milton arrived at Giles-Chalfont in July 1665 just after Thomas Ellwood, Isaac Penington and many others attending the funeral of a beloved Friend, were seized and imprisoned for a month in Aylesbury Prison. Legend, rather than documentary evidence, credits Guli Springett with visiting the great poet that summer at his cottage (only a mile from her home), reading and singing to him in his blindness. It would seem the normal and neighborly thing to do and could well be true.

When Penington and Ellwood were released from prison the younger man made haste to call upon his "quondam master," Milton. The poet gave him a manuscript to read which he took home with him to the Grange and there "[when I] had set myself to read it, I found it was that excellent Poem which he entituled *Paradise Lost.*"

One can but wonder whether Guli Springett read the manuscript of "that excellent Poem" while it was under her roof.[13]

Soon prison walls again closed around Guli's stepfather. He had been home scarce a month when seized "by military Force and carried Prisoner to Aylesbury Goal again, where he lay three-quarters of a year."

Shortly after that "his wife and Family were turned out of his house called the Grange at Peter's-Chalfont by them who had seized upon his Estate." For a time the family scattered. "Mary Penington with her younger children went down to her husband at Aylesbury. Guli, with her maid, went to Bristol to see her former maid Anne Hersent who was married to a Merchant of that City and I," says Thomas Ellwood, "went to Aylesbury with the children . . . and after some time went to Bristol to conduct Guli home."

Arriving home from Bristol Guli found that her mother had rented a farm house "called Bottrels, in the Parish of Giles-Chalfont." Eventually Ellwood secured larger and better lodgings for the family at Amersham "whither we went at Michaelmas [September 29, 1666], having spent most of the summer at the other Place [Bottrells]."

Cast down by this gypsy life, Mary Penington considered returning to her estates in Kent, but her husband demurred. They had many friends in Buckinghamshire who knew what they had suffered and respected them for it. She finally decided to sell one of her farms in Kent and therewith purchase Woodside House at Amersham, much in need of renovation. This place she rebuilt and lived in for the rest of her life.[14]

It was during these unsettled years of hardship for the Peningtons, as for all Friends, that George Fox, the great Quaker leader, was released in 1666 from a two year imprisonment in Scarborough Castle and began "journeys under concern" to establish some form of organization among the Quaker meetings.

Fox's *Journal* shows that late in 1667 he organized the mens' monthly meeting in Buckinghamshire near the Peningtons—

and Thomas Ellwood mentions having attended that meeting. In the next sentence Ellwood says

"And afterwards I traveled with Guli and her maid into the West of England, to meet him there, and to visit Friends in those parts; and we went as far as Topsham, in Devonshire, before we found him. He had been in Cornwall and was then returning . . . we turned back with him through Devonshire, Somersetshire, and Dorsetshire, having generally very good meetings where he was . . . "[15]

It was in July of 1668 that Guli and Ellwood caught up with the traveling Quaker minister at Topsham and joined him in his travels from meeting to meeting throughout southern England to London. "By the time we came back from this journey," says Ellwood, "the summer was pretty far gone."

Upon his return Thomas Ellwood began paying court to a worthy and well-heeled Quakeress some years his senior who soon became his wife.

Sometime during 1668, reportedly in London, Guli met him "for whom she was reserved."

William Penn

"He For Whom She Was Reserved"

William Penn, son of Admiral Sir William Penn, had been a precocious child, reading his Bible intently and experiencing religious ecstasies at a tender age. His father educated him for the life of a courtier, a calling for which William Penn's later life proved his ample gifts. But to him the life of the spirit held by far the greatest value. His unworldly determination at the age of twenty-three, to devote himself to the Lord as a Quaker minister, was a bitter blow to the ambitions of his father, the admiral. Yet Sir William forgave him and bequeathed generous wealth to this incomprehensible son.

William Penn first heard a Quaker preacher when he was but a child, living with his father in Cork (1655). This man was Thomas Loe who later convinced him of the truth. Some years afterwards (1662) William Penn first aroused his father's rage by being expelled from Oxford for non-conformity. "Bitter usage I underwent when I returned to my father, whipping, beating, and turning out of doors in 1662."[16]

Sent to France for courtly polish, the young Penn studied

under the great Protestant divine, Moise Amyraut at the Huguenot College in Saumur. At home again he studied law for two years at Lincolns Inn Court, London. His father then sent him to Ireland to secure experience as a soldier. As a soldier he did well, but alas for the admiral's ambition! In Ireland he again heard the Quaker Thomas Loe who had so much impressed him in his childhood.

When a soldier came to break up a Quaker meeting he was attending in Ireland September 3, 1667, William Penn "takes him by ye collar and would have throw'd him down stairs," not yet having fully learned the Quaker tenant of non-resistance, but Friends restrained his worldly roughness. The soldier brought officers who took Penn and others to prison. The Harvey chronicle says "as he went to prison he gave his sword to his man & never wore one after."[17]

Influential friends soon got Penn out of prison and sent word to his father who ordered him home. By October 22 (1667) the young man had not yet appeared in London when his father wrote again urging no delay.[18] It is from the Harvey chronicle we learn that he had landed at Bristol and spent a while in that vicinity attending Quaker meetings to strengthen himself against his father's wrath. Josiah Coale of Winterbourne, near Bristol, then went with him to his father's house to soften the admiral's rage. Admiral Penn spoke civilly in the presence of Coale.

Perhaps the thread of destiny may be seen in this sustaining presence of Josiah Coale, possibly the only Quaker then in England who had traversed the land later to become Pennsylvania. Coale had been twice to the Indian towns on the Susquehanna River in the area now Lancaster County, Pennsylvania. His first visit had been in August 1658. He went again (1660) at the urging of George Fox, to ask the Susquehannock Indians' permission to settle a Quaker colony upon the Susquehanna. From his memory of these voyages Josiah Coale could tell Penn of a land beyond the sea toward which even as a youth at Oxford the young man had had "an opening of joy."[19]

Picture the three in Admiral Penn's London parlor—the forceful admiral, all his hopes and ambitions centered upon a distinguished public career for his beloved son, controling his wrath before Josiah Coale, an unworldly soul who had seen the land of dreams beyond the sea—and between them the gifted young Penn for whose future they contended.

Although the admiral "kept his temper while J. Coale was there," he later berated William for using *thee* and *thou* and "as he was going upstairs to bed his father bid him rise in the morning for he should go out in his coach with him wch caused Wm to be so uneasy that he could not sleep."

In the morning, however, his father at first tried merely the effects of sweet reasoning, to which William could only answer that he must obey "the manifestations of God in his own conscience." As they passed a tavern on the way home from the early morning drive Admiral Penn suggested a glass of wine: "when they came into the Room his Father lock'd the Door then William expected to be caned but instead of that his Father laying his hands on the table told him he would kneel down and pray to God that he might not be a Quaker nor go to any more of there meetings: Wm open'd the Casement and sayd before he would hear his Father pray after that manner he would leep out at winder . . . "

At that instant a knock on the door broke the impasse. A nobleman who had seen the Penn coach parked outside the tavern came in to chat. This gentleman told Admiral Penn that "he might think himself happy in a son that could Dispise the Grandure of the world and refrain from the many vices . . . which very much encouraged Wm . . . "[20]

Other eminent persons made similar remarks to Penn's father which for a time alleviated his alarm about this "wild Rambling Colt."[21]

Gulielma Springett and William Penn 1668

It could scarcely have been in the mirey time of winter that Guli, her maid and Thomas Ellwood set out on horseback to find George Fox on his preaching tour of southern England. It would have been in fair weather when "longen folk to goon on pilgrimages" as Chaucer hath it.

At this very time, according to the Harvey chronicle, William Penn went out with Friends upon a similar jaunt.[22] As they rode through the blooming English countryside William exuberantly snatched off his wig and threw it behind him, never looking back to see where it landed. "He had some hair tho' but short . . . "

And in this spring of 1668 "they had a meeting where Wm's

Mouth was first open'd then went to several other places the Magistrate knowing who Wm was sent to one of the Secretarys how Wm with other were causeing tumults by preaching the Quakers Doctrine at this his Father . . . sent him orders to return home the friend he was with advised him to obey his Father's order which after some little time he did, coming to London went to a meeting before he went to see his Father after meeting went up into the Room where a Friend brought Guli Springett wch was the first time he saw her who was afterwards his wife."

Guli Springett and William Penn were the same age, both born in 1644. William would not reach his twenty-fourth birthday until October, but Guli had passed hers in February. This fateful encounter moments before he faced his angry father surely gave William strength for the ordeal. The family uproar later that day and defeat of the male parent is well conveyed by the contemporary account:

" . . . Returning home his father told he had heard what work he had been making in the country and after some discourse his Father told him to take his cloaths and be Gon from his house . . . also that he should dispose of his Estate to them that pleased him better Wm gave his Father to understand how great a cross 'twas to him to disoblige his Father not in regard to his Estate but from the Filial affection he bore him but as he was convinced of the Truth he must be faithfull so Go's up stairs and packt up a small bundle comes down again saluts his Mother and Sister then tell his Father how unpleasant his Displeasure was to him but should always think himself obliged to pray for his Father so left his father's house only with his small bundle as he went out of the house heard Great cry's by his mother and sister but was not Got far before a servant was sent for him to return when he return'd his Father was gon out of the way so he got to his Room till his Father's displeasure was something abated . . . "[23]

In a short time the Penn family repeated this performance, resulting in William's short absence from home "having no other Subsistence except what his Mother privately sent him." However, "his steady Perseverance evincing his Integrity his Father's wrath became somewhat mollified, so that he winked at his return to and continuance in his Family."[24]

From the moment of William Penn's meeting with Guli Springett his life began to follow the pattern of her beloved

step-father's, Isaac Penington: parental displeasure and re-
jection, involvement with Friends, preaching, writing Friends'
tracts, imprisonment, writing in prison, court battles, in a
continuous cycle. With all this Guli was familiar. It had been
a part of her life since childhood: to her it was the noblest work
of man, and in her eyes William Penn was certainly a knight
in the shining armor of Light. Few indeed were the ladies of
her age, quality (and beauty) who could have given the idealistic
William Penn such complete sympathy, understanding and
approval.

With two weighty Friends, Josiah Coale and George Whitehead, young William Penn went more than once to the court
of Charles II in the autumn of 1668 to urge liberation and
toleration for banished Quakers.[25]

A letter has survived that he wrote to Guli Springett in
October 1668 telling of the death of his father-in-the-faith,
Thomas Loe, and another to Isaac Penington on the same
subject.[26]

That fateful year of 1668 William Penn wrote his first Quaker
pamphlets, *Truth Exalted* and *Sandy Foundations Shaken*. The
unorthodoxy of the *Sandy Foundations* so offended the clergy
that he was imprisoned in the Tower of London for nine
months, December 1668 to August 1669. In the Tower he
industriously produced pamphlets, among them *No Cross
No Crown*, one of his three most noteworthy books.

He was in solitary confinement in a cold and dismal cell,
allowed quill, ink and paper to express his thoughts, but no
letters to or from friends. *The British Calendar of State Papers*
lists a permit issued to his servant December 24, 1668 "for
Francis Cooke to see Wm Penn his Master close prisoner in the
Tower and to speake with him in the presence of a Keeper."[27]

In the presence of the prison keeper Penn gave Cooke a
verbal message to his father and Guli Springett. The message,
as Cooke afterwards wrote it to Guli, is found among the
Penn Papers at the Historical Society of Pennsylvania:

Dr G.S.
*I thought it convenient to send thee a copy of what my Masters Reply
was to me, when I brought him word, how that the Bishop of London
would have him recant in Comen garden, at an appointed time, before
the Face of all the City, or else be a Prisoner during his Life.*
Saith he, all is well, I wish they had told me so before, since the ex-

pecting of a release put a stop to some Business. Thou mayst tell my Father, who, I know, will ask thee, these words, that my Prison shall be my grave before I will budge a jot, for I ow my conscience to no mortall man . . .[28]

Guli's Trip to Sussex 1669

While William Penn assiduously applied quill pen to paper in the Tower of London all through the summer of 1669, Guli Springett and Thomas Ellwood again took horse to journey over the countryside. They went first to London. Perhaps they were able to transmit some cheer of word or creature comfort to the prisoner in the Tower. Thomas is careful to make it clear that he took this trip to protect Guli, at her mother's request. And nobly did he preserve her from jostling, capers and practical jokes of rude fellows who wore the livery of the Duke of York.

"The occasion of this journey was to accompany Mary Penington's daughter, Guli, to her uncle Springett's in Sussex, and from thence among her tenants. We tarried at London the first Night, and set out next Morning on the Tunbridge Road, and Seven-Oak lying in our Way, we put in there to bait; But truly, we had much ado to get either Provisions or Room for ourselves or our Horses, the House was so filled with Guests, and those not of the better Sort. For the Duke of York being . . . on the Road that Day for the Wells, divers of his Guards, and the meaner sort of his Retinue, had near filled all the Inns there.

"I left John Gigger who waited on Guli in this journey to take Care for the Horses . . . I got a little Room to put her into, and having shut her into it, went to see what Relief the Kitchen would afford us; and with much ado, by praying hard and paying dear, I got a small Joint of Meat from the Spit, which served rather to stay than satisfy our Stomachs, for we were all pretty sharp set.

"After this short Repast . . . we quickly mounted and took the Road again, willing to hasten from a Place where we found nothing but Rudeness, for the Roysters who swarmed there, besides the damning Oaths they belched out at one another, looked very sourly on us, as if they grudged both the Horses we rode and the Cloaths we wore.

"A Knot of these soon followed us . . . We had a Spot of fine smooth sandy Way, whereon the Horses trod so softly that we heard them not till one of them was upon us. I was then riding abreast with Guli, and discoursing with her when on a sudden, hearing a little Noise and turning mine Eye that Way, I saw an Horseman coming up on the further side of her Horse, having his left Arm stretched out just ready to take her about the Waste and pluck her off backwards from her own horse, to lay her before him on his. I had but just Time to thrust forth my Stick between him and her, and bid him stand off . . . His horse being nimble, he slipt by me, and got up to her on the near Side, to prevent which, I thrust in upon him again, and in our jostling we drove her Horse quite out of the Way, and almost into the next Hedge.

"While we were thus contending I heard a Noise of loud Laughter behind us, and turning my Head that Way I saw three or four Horse-men more, who could scarce sit their Horses for laughing, to see the Sport. Their Companion . . . had in his Hand a short thick Truncheon which he held up at me, on which, laying hold with a strong Gripe I suddenly wrenched it out of his Hand and threw it at as far a Distance behind me as I could.

"While he rode back to fetch his Truncheon, I called up honest John Gigger who was indeed of a Temper so thoroughly peaceable that he had not hitherto put in at all. But now I rouzed him and bid him ride close up to his Mistress's Horse on the further side so that no Horse might thrust in between. But he, good Man, not thinking it decent for him to ride so near his Mistress, left room enough for another to ride between. And indeed, so soon as our Brute had recovered his Truncheon, he came up directly thither and had thrust in again had not I, by a nimble Turn, chopt in upon him and kept him at Bay . . ."

The encounter now became a battle of words, with the merry companions pulling their friend from the fray and apologizing that "he had drunk a little too liberally."

"When we came to Tunbridge I set John Gigger foremost, bidding him lead on briskly through the Town, and placing Guli in the Middle, I came up close after her that I might both observe and interpose if any fresh Abuse should have been offered her. We were expected I perceived, for though it rained very hard the Street was thronged with Men who looked very earnestly on us, but did not put any Affront upon us.

"We had a good way to ride beyond Tunbridge and beyond

the Wells in By-ways among the Woods, and were the later for Hindrance we had had on the way. And when, being come to Harbert Springett's House, Guli acquainted her Uncle what Trouble and Danger she had gone through on the Way, he resented it so high, that he would have had the Persons prosecuted for it. But since Providence had interposed and so well preserved and delivered her, she chose to pass by the Offence.

"When Guli had finished the Business she went upon we returned home and I delivered her to her glad Mother."[29]

It was on this journey that Guli signed the contract (July 22, 1669) with her tenant John Fuller which still survives at Friends House, London.

Courtship and Marriage 1669–1672

Guli had not been home long from her business trip to Sussex before William Penn was freed from the Tower and stopped off to visit the Penington family at Bury Farm near Amersham on his way to Ireland. He and Guli Springett with others walked to Quaker meetings in the neighborhood through the cool September weather. When he rode with the Penington men and boys to visit the Quaker prisoners in Reading Goal Guli and Thomas Ellwood accompanied them part way. But the autobiography of Thomas Ellwood, so full of detail when he is protecting Guli Springett, never mentions the name of William Penn in connection with her until William Penn is in America and Thomas is again called upon to help Guli in distress. Penn's visit with the Peningtons in September 1669 is referred to only in his own brief diary notes.

These notes indicate that he wrote to Guli and received letters from her while he was in Ireland from October 1669 to July 1670 looking after business matters for both his father and Guli, as well as concerning himself seriously with the affairs of troubled Friends there. In June of 1670 his diary entries refer to her tenderly as "my o.d.ff." and "my o.b.ff." (my own dear friend, my own best friend).[30]

It is strange how few of Guli Springett's letters survive. I have found reference to only four, three of them addressed to Margaret Fox, and the other one to William Penn on this visit to Ireland. The later, dated July 16, 1670, survived only because William Penn never received it; it was intercepted en route and has remained since 1670 among the papers of the

Public Records Office, London, with it enclosures from the two Mary Peningtons, Guli's mother and young half-sister, indicating that they long to see young John Penington who had gone with Penn to Ireland.[31]

Guli speaks of another brother, Isaac Penington, aged 18, whom they are daily expecting home from a voyage to Barbados. This promising youth they never saw again for, as the ship sailed home in a brisk gale, he fell overboard and was lost at sea.[32]

The year 1670 saw strict enforcement of the Conventicle Act, prohibiting dissenters to meet for worship. Back in London, in August, when William Penn found the doors and windows of his meetinghouse boarded shut by the authorities, he and William Meade preached to the congregation outside the meetinghouse, in the street. They were both arrested August 14, 1670, charged with inciting to riot, and committed to Newgate prison.

At the trial the first week of September William Penn conducted his own defence. The jury refused to find the prisoners guilty as they were instructed to do by the judge. For this the judge fined the jury and locked them up. The jury, finally released on a writ of habeas corpus, sued the mayor and recorder for illegal imprisonment. Final decision, in the Court of Common Pleas, with twelve judges on the bench: "juries must not be coerced in reaching or giving their verdict." This famous Penn-Meade trial established the right of juries to bring in a verdict from the evidence, uninfluenced by the will of the judge—a basic right in American and English law today.[33]

Following the initial trial William Penn remained in prison refusing to pay a fine, but someone—possibly his mother—paid the fine, for Sir William was on his deathbed and longed to see his son. William closed his father's eyes in peace September 16, 1670.[34]

The next few months he spent in Buckinghamshire, near Amersham, writing three books, engaging in public dispute with a Baptist adversary, and undoubtedly calling frequently at the Penington home.[35]

But "it was a cruel, bloody, persecuting time." February 5, 1671 William was arrested for preaching at a meeting in Wheeler Street, London. On this occasion he spent six months in the foul prison of Newgate, busily employed writing treatises and letters to those in authority. He also wrote verse (notable more for sentiment than genius) which he sent to Gulielma Maria Springett, beginning

> Your Goals & Prisons we defie
> By bonds we'l keep our Libertie
> Nor shall your racks or torments make
> Us e're our Meetings to forsake . . .[36]

Penn's six month prison term expired in August 1671, just in time for him to see George Fox off on a voyage to America. William Penn, Guli Springett, her mother Mary Penington and Margaret Fox, wife of the preacher, went with George Fox "from James Strut's in Wapping in one of the Kinge's Barges to the Ship." Fox stayed aboard that night, but "the company with William Penn lodged at Gravesend." Early in the morning they came aboard. The ship weighed anchor, sailed briskly all day from Gravesend to the Downs where William Penn, Guli, Mary Penington and Margaret took leave of George Fox and went ashore. George Fox, the founder of Quakerism, was on his way to America in the footsteps of Josiah Coale, and William Penn was the last to shake his departing hand.[37]

At about this time William Penn presented to Guli a copy of a book he had worked on during his imprisonment at Newgate, *An Apology for the Principles and Practices of the People Called Quakers*, by George Whitehead and William Penn, bound in calf, inscribed on the fly leaf in William Penn's own hand, "To my deare ffriend Gulielma Springett," and below intertwined initials, "WP."[38]

Soon after this Penn traveled briefly in Holland and Germany; returning he arranged all preliminaries for his marriage with Gulielma Maria Springett. These included drawing up a marriage settlement concerning their estates and consideration of the nuptial proceedings in two sessions of the Friends Monthly Meeting for the Upper Side of the County of Bucks held at Ellwood's home, Hunger Hill. The records of these meetings are all in Ellwood's neat handwriting as is the original marriage certificate of William and Guli Penn dated April 2, 1672 when they did "Solemnly and expressly take each other in marriage, mutually promising to be loving, true & faithful to each other in that Relation so long as it shal please the Lord to continue their naturel lives." This certificate was signed in a Friends' Meeting at King John's Farm, Chorley Wood, Hertfordshire, by forty-six witnesses, including Lady Penn, Guli's mother Mary Penington, and her stepfather, Isaac Penington. And the "mariage has been crowned with a continued affection," wrote John Aubrey during Guli's lifetime.[39]

Basing House, Rickmansworth 1672–1675

For his bride William Penn rented Basing House, Rickmansworth, Hertfordshire, not six miles from her mother, and there he took her in a new coach he had purchased for the occasion.

In the year of his marriage Penn published a *Treatise on Oaths* and *England's Present Interest Considered.* In the fall of the year he went upon a preaching mission through "Kent, Sussex, & the Skirt of Surrey," leaving Guli in the meantime with his mother, Lady Penn, at Watford in Hertfordshire.

After a month of "strong and sound" meetings in the home counties of Guli's parents, Penn and his missionary companion felt "it rise in the liberty & sweet Love of the Lord in both our Hearts to go home to our Dear Wives & Families, which we accomplisht that Day . . . I went by Kingston . . . cross the Country to my Dear Wife & got home before the 7th hour in the evening being about 20 miles . . ."[40]

Guli's anonymous spiritual influence upon these best years in the life of William Penn cannot be calculated. She was with him when he met George Fox at Bristol in July of 1673 upon the return of that indefatiguable minister from his American journey. It was the time of the great fair in Bristol, many people gathered there and the Friends held "glorious and powerful meetings." Fox spent the next few months in various counties of England "where he had many large and precious meetings, and much service in the gospel ministry."[41] Towards winter Fox, with his wife and her daughter Rachel, came to "William Penns at Rickmansworth whither Thomas Lower, who had married another of my wife's daughters, came the next day to accompany us on our journey northwards."[42] Surely on this visit, and many other times in meetings with George Fox, Guli's interest glowed brightly as William Penn's while they discoursed with Fox the dream of a Quaker refuge in America.

Fox and his family left the Penns at Rickmansworth in December for their journey home but had gotten only as far as Worcester when Fox was seized and imprisoned for refusing to take an oath. More than a year's strenuous exertion on the part of his friends, and William Penn's influence at court, finally led to the faulty indictment being quashed. Fox was freed early in 1675 and never again imprisoned.[43] From Swarthmoor Hall Margaret Fox sent Guli Penn a gift of home made bread in a straw case.[44]

John Aubrey, reporting current comment during Guli's lifetime, said that she was the image of her father "in person and qualities, virtuous, generous, wise, humble, plaine; generally beloved for those good qualities and one more—the great cures she does, having great skill in physic and surgery, which she freely bestows . . ."[45]

A copy of Guli's book of cures, in addition to the recipes of cookery herein printed, is among the Penn Manuscripts at the Historical Society of Pennsylvania. It must certainly have come from her grandmother Springett (née Partridge) who was even more famous in her day for the same gift, employing several women to prepare ointments from herbs for use in physic, surgery and for eyes, frequently having as many as twenty patients at a time waiting for her attention.[46]

Unhappily, Guli's skill in cures failed in her own family. Of her eight children (including twins), only William and Laetitia outlived both parents. William married and left descendants, but died fairly young of a consumption. Springett, the gifted child who gave promise of following in his parents' footsteps, barely survived his mother. The others died in infancy.[47]

After three of their children and Penn's brother Richard had died at Rickmansworth, the Penns left their honeymoon house with its subsequent dismal memories. Springett Penn was born January 25, 1676 at the home of his grandmother, Margaret Jasper Penn, and soon after the family moved to Worminghurst in Sussex, home county of the Springett family.[48] Worminghurst immediately became the gathering place of large Quaker meetings.

Worminghurst and the American Dream 1676–1682

According to the Haistwell Diary, George Fox came to Worminghurst from London with William Penn on June

20th, 1677, making the Penns' home his headquarters for three weeks while he, with William Penn, George Keith and others had meetings up and down the country. Two of the meetings were held at Worminghurst with hundreds of people attending.[49]

July 8 "there was a meeting at W.P.s where there was many Fds as also several hundreds of people: at which meeting" George Fox, Isaac Penington, George Keith, John Burnyeat and William Penn "declared the truth, all being very peaceable."

At Worminghurst on July 12 again hundreds of people. Friends brought George Fox a rumor that informers would come to the meeting, ". . . . he bid them bee chearfull, and not fear them, so G.F. walked into the Garden, and when the Meeting was settled hee went into the meeting . . . but no Informers did appear and so the Meeting ended in peace."

The next day George Fox took leave of the Penn family, "W.P. accompanying G.F. 12 miles in his Coach . . ."

At other times the family led a quiet life. "In summer they rose at five, in winter at seven, in spring and autumn at six . . . They had breakfast at nine, dinner at twelve, supper at seven and to bed at ten. They assembled with the servants for worship in the morning; and at eleven to make a recess in the work of the forenoon they met again for reading the Bible and other religious books. At six in the evening they met again for religious worship . . . After supper the servants reported on what they had done, and received orders for the next day. 'Loud discourse and troublesome noise were forbidden. All quarrels were to be made up before bedtime.' "[50]

"Sufferings continued very sore and heavy upon friends not only in the city, but in most parts of the nation."[51] The sore straits of their imprisoned friends, the heavy confiscatory fines laid upon many others, the harried lives of the faithful — all this created a danger that the friendly persuasion might be obliterated. Many Friends had already found refuge in New Jersey, on the eastern coast of North America. Penn had been a trustee and counsellor concerned in this area, and of course the troubles of Friends had always been of deep concern to Guli. Fox had dreamed of a haven in America for more than twenty years. Now the dream of a refuge was taking shape in reality.[52] We need not repeat in detail here the well known story of the Stuarts' debt to Admiral Penn, their friendship for the admiral's son, and the great grant of wild, uncultivated land beyond the sea which Charles II bestowed upon William Penn to settle the claim.

To Pennsylvania 1682

On the fifth of March, 1681 Penn wrote jubilantly, "this day my country was confirmed to me under the great seal of England, with large powers and privileges, by the name of Pennsylvania, a name the King would give it in honour of my father . . ."[53]

While forming an outline of government, and selling tracts in his province at London in 1681, Penn was aflame with dreams of a country to be populated by good men who would leave all evil behind them when they set sail from the crowded ports of Europe for a virgin land of hope in the west. It was God's work and Penn prayed "that an example may be sett upp to the nations—There may be room there tho not here for such an Holy Experiment . . . mine eye is to a blessed Government, & a Virtuous, Ingenous & Industrious Society, so as People may live well and have more time to serve the Lord than in this crowded land—God will plant America."[54]

At this time there were three children in the Penn family at Worminghurst, Springett born 1676, Laetitia, 1679 and William, Jr. who arrived a week after the granting of the Pennsylvania charter. While their father's time was filled to overflowing with the affairs of the new province, Guli's family duties were equally arduous. Besides the small children who absorb a mother's full time care, the older members of the family were frail and needed tender attention. Isaac Penington died at one of his wife's farms in Kent while there with her on a business trip in 1679. William Penn's mother lay sick unto death at Worminghurst and passed away there in 1682 a few months before her son left for America. Guli's mother was ill at Worminghurst when her son-in-law sailed in the *Welcome*.[55]

The American adventure was surely one which Guli and William Penn had planned together. Her fortune as well as his was eventually committed to the Pennsylvania project.[56] The plans for departure in 1682 progressed; many persons were ready to go with the proprietor; his sailing could not be delayed, but Guli Penn's mother, Mary Penington, was in her last illness and Guli, though she may not have mentioned it, was again expecting "a little one." Guli could not sail on the *Welcome* in 1682 but she would come as soon as possible to join her husband in their Holy Experiment. William Penn assured Margaret Fox "my dear wife . . . is sweetly consenting and satisfied . . ."⁵⁷

Before he left Worminghurst Penn wrote the affectionate paragraph which opens this account of Guli's life, with several pages more of good advice about conduct and care of the children. For their education he recommended:

"Above all things, endeavour to breed them up in the love of virtue and that holy, plain way of it which we have lived in, that the world in no part of it get into my family. I had rather they were homely than finely bred as to outward behaviour: yet I love sweetness, mixed with gravity, and cheerfulness tempered with sobriety. Religion in the heart leads into this true civility, teaching men and women to be mild and courteous in their behaviour . . .

"Breed them up in a love of one another; tell them it is a charge I left behind me . . . For their learning be liberal. Spare no cost: for by such parsimony all is lost that is saved; but let it be useful knowledge, such as is consistent with truth and godliness, not cherishing a vain conversation or idle mind, but ingenuity mixed with industry is good for the body and mind too. I recommend the useful parts of mathematics, as building houses or ships, measuring, surveying, dialling, navigation; but agriculture is specially in my eye; let my children be husbandmen and housewives; it is industrious, healthy, honest, and of good example . . .

"When grown big, have most care for them; for then there are more snares, both within and without. When marriageable, see that they have worthy persons in their eye, of good life, and good fame for piety and understanding. I need no wealth but sufficiency and be sure that their love be dear, fervent, and mutual, that it may be happy for them. I choose not that they may be married to earthly, covetous kindred; and of cities and towns of concourse beware; the world is apt to stick close to those who have lived and got wealth there; a country life and estate I like best for my children. I prefer a decent mansion, of an hundred pounds per annum, before ten thousand pounds in London, or such like place, in a way of trade . . ."

To the children he left as his parting message:

". . . Be obedient to your dear mother, a woman whose virtue and good name is an honour to you; for she hath been exceeded by none in her time for her plainness, integrity, industry, humanity, virtue, and good understanding—qualities not usual among women of her worldly condition and quality. Therefore honour and obey her, my dear children, as your mother and your father's love and delight; nay, love her too, for she loved your father with a dear and upright love, choosing him before all her many suitors; and though she be of a delicate constitution and noble spirit, yet she descended to the utmost tenderness and care for you, performing the painfulest acts of service for you in your infancy, as a mother and a nurse too. I charge you, before the Lord, honour and obey, love and cherish your dear mother . . ."

The *Epitome of the Weekly News,* London, carried a small news item under dateline of Deal, August 29, 1682 "Being Wednesday, the Wind East North East, William Penn Esq., Sole Proprietor and Governor of Pennsilvania went on board the *Welcome,* in order to his Voyage for that Province, accompanied with his wife and others to Dover Road, where they parted."[58]

If tradition be accurate, Penn had with him a blue fringed silk net sash made by Guli which he wore when meeting with the Indians at Shackamaxon.[59] And Guli's American keepsake was surely a Spanish gold piece of Ferdinand and Isabella, given her by Lady Penn, William's mother.[60]

Guli Alone at Worminghurst 1682–1684

From Deal Guli returned to her children and to her mother lying ill at Worminghurst. Mary Penington died within two weeks after the *Welcome* sailed. She is buried beside Isaac Penington at Jordans, Chalfont. Her landed estate she willed to the young Peningtons: "As my daughter Penn hath a large proportion of this world's substance and my latter children have not anything, I find it my duty to provide for them . . . to my daughter Gulielma Maria Penn, her choice of a suit of damask (table linen) except that marked I.M.P."[61]

The account of her life which Mary Penington had written so carefully for her daughter Guli and her grandson Springett was unaccountably tucked away, either by her own hand or that of another, behind the wainscoting in a room at Worming-hurst, and there found many years later, possibly at the time the house was demolished.[62]

"Guli Penn is safe delivered of a daught: and its like she will be ready to go for Pennsylvania in ye 7th or 8th month." so wrote James Claypoole to Benjamin Furly March 13, 1683.[63]

On August 21st Guli herself wrote to Margaret Fox, "I was very weak a long time after my lying in and it pleased the Lord to take away my little one, when it was about three weeks old. It was a mighty great child and it was near dead when it was born, which I think it never got over. Dear George Fox came a-purpose to see me . . ."

Guli had been very ill indeed. In this same letter she tells of being stricken with St. Anthony's fire (erysipelas) in her face and eyes. She sent Margaret Fox a letter she had just received from William Penn telling of large meetings in Phila-delphia, as many as three hundred attending, adding, "I ex-pect to hear shortly what my Husband will have me to doe whether I shall goe this yeare or no but feare if he does send I shall scarse be well enough yett to goe."[64]

James Ellwood, whose writings are strangely silent con-cerning Guli after 1669, reported happily that in 1683 when William Penn was in America she sent for him, she needed his help:

"I received advice, by an Express out of Sussex, that Guli Penn . . . was very dangerously ill, her husband being then absent in Pennsylvania and that she had a great Desire to see and speak with me . . . I took Horse and went so far that Evening towards Worminghurst, that I got thither pretty early next Morning, and to my great Satisfaction, found my Friend in a hopeful way towards a recovery. I staid some days with her; and then finding her Illness wear daily off, and some other Friends being come from London to visit her, . . . I took my leave of her and them . . ."

It must have been in the spring of 1684 that Guli, expected daily in Pennsylvania, wrote again to Margaret Fox of her difficulties:

"I delayed writing to thee in the hope of giving thee a fuller account of my husband and of our going. But the winter and spring have been so severe that letters have been hindered; and now that many are come, none of them of late dates are for me because my husband has been in daily expectation of seeing us there, and I am sorry for his disappointment . . . the Friend who does our business here being under some trouble . . . [I] know not where to get another that is fit to leave things to at present, which is a great strait to my mind; my husband writing every letter for us . . ."[65]

August 2, 1684 Guli wrote to Margaret that "there have been great reports of my husband coming . . . This puts a stop at present to my going . . ."[66]

William Penn, that very week in far off Philadelphia, wrote (August 6) his will and another farewell letter to his wife and family before setting out in the little *Endeavour* for the return trip to England.[67] Business about his southern boundary line and other affairs of his province required his personal attention in London. When he wrote Margaret Fox of his arrival home he thanked her for friendship to Guli during his absence.[68]

The Last Years 1685–1694

The little information we have of Guli Penn henceforth shows her wholly involved with her husband in Quaker activities at home and in London. Only three glimpses have survived for the year 1685, the first a certificate she and her husband signed August 2 attesting the good character of Elizabeth Simms upon her departure for Pennsylvania.[69]

Then, through the Itinerary Journal of George Fox, we see her at London in late August when Fox "went with W.P. & his wife in their Coach to their Lodgings at Chering Cross . . . & from thence he & Guly Penn went to visit Widdow Birkit beyond the water but She was not at home Soe having stayd a while they went from thence to her Sisters where they stayd & dined . . ."[70]

In November, 1685, slightly more than a year after Penn's return, Gulielma bore her eighth and last child, named for her, Gulielma Maria, a child who remained with the family at Worminghurst four years before joining the other Penn infants in the Jordans grave yard.[71]

In March of 1687 Guli entertained the Womens' Quarterly Meeting of Sussex at Worminghurst.[72]

We catch sight of Guli twice more through the *Journal* of George Fox, first in July 1688 when William Penn and his wife came to the home of William Meade, and from there the next day Fox went with them in their coach to a meeting where William Penn, Fox and others declared the truth "to the Refreshment of many there. It was a very Large Meeting there being a great Many friends from London & a great great Many of the worlds people from the adjacent places & after a while he took Coatch to WMs agn where WP & his wife & Son & a great many more friends Dined & after went away that Night."[73]

The final mention of Guli Penn in Fox's journal is in April 1689, two years before he died. It concerned a meeting "at Gracious Street" where William Penn and George Fox "Declared a pritty time" and when they had done "the Meeting Departed which was very Large thence he (Fox) went to Henry Goldney's again, being weary and very weak, and W.P. & his Wife and severall other friends Came to visit him there . . ."[74]

Rapid changes in the political scene prevented the Penn family migration to Pennsylvania which they constantly planned. The death of Charles II brought his avowedly catholic brother James II to the throne of England. Through his personal friendship with both these kings Penn tirelessly worked to secure toleration for the religious minorities which were being harried by the power of the established church. When Parliament expelled the catholic James and called his protestant daughter Mary to the throne with her husband William of Orange, enemies of Penn's toleration activities used his friendship for the Stuart kings as a means to discredit him with the new regime.

In January 1691 when Penn had a ship engaged to take him and his to Pennsylvania, George Fox died and Penn, giving the principal sermon at the services, narrowly missed imprisonment by a constable who had mistaken the hour of the funeral and came too late. His loyalty lay under a cloud of unwarranted suspicion. Time and again after the accession of William and Mary he was obliged to prove in court his innocence of any plots to aid the banished monarch. The crown sent a royal governor to Pennsylvania and in 1692 confiscated his province.[75]

To avoid unwelcome government attention, Penn went into seclusion for three years (1691–1693). His serenity of mind unruffled, he utilized this period of obscurity to produce further admirable books and pamphlets. Little concerning Guli emerges from these abeyant years. There can be no doubt that Penn's serenity and peace of mind, under the severe afflictions of his public life, derived directly from the domestic felicity, unswerving loyalty, and spiritual harmony he found with his wife Gulielma.

Finally, in November 1693, the royal government gave to Penn a full and public acquittal of all the charges and accusations against him. Penn wrote to Thomas Lloyd in Pennsylvania, ". . . the secretary . . . having it from King William's own mouth . . . told me I was as free as ever . . . and he discharged me on the 30th. From the secretary I went to our meeting at the Bull and Mouth; thence to visit the sanctuary of my solitude; and after to see my poor wife and children."[76]

The Penn family hoped to resume plans for speedy removal to Pennsylvania, but the strain of the past few years had been too much for Gulielma. She had been very ill during most of Penn's eclipse, for six months in 1692 and again for the latter half of 1693, revived briefly at the news of his vindication in November so that Penn wrote to friends in Philadelphia just before Christmas, "My wife is yet weakly; but I am not without hopes of her recovery, who is of the best of wives and women."[77]

During these last days "she would not suffer me, after I recovered my liberty, to neglect any public meeting upon her account, saying often, 'Oh! go, dearest, do not hinder any good for me. I desire thee go; I have cast my care upon the Lord; I shall see thee again.' "[78]

In the printed memorial of her last hours composed by Penn he wrote sadly,

"She did at several times pray very sweetly and in all her Weakness manifested the most equal, undaunted and resigned Spirit . . . she was an excelling Person, both as Child, Wife, Mother, Mistress, Friend and Neighbour . . .

"Speaking solemnly to the children she said . . . I never desired any Great Things for you, but that you may fear the Lord, and walk in his Truth among his People to the end of your days . . .

". . . about an hour after, causing all to withdraw, we were half an hour together, in which we took our last leave, saying all that was fit upon that solemn Occasion. She continued Sensible, and eat something about an hour before her Departure, at which time our Children, and most of the Family, were present, she quietly Expired in my Arms, her Head upon my Bosom, with a sensible and Devout Resignation of her Soul to Almighty God.

"I hope I may say, she was a Publick, as well as Private Loss, for she was not only an excellent Wife and Mother, but an Entire and Constant Friend, of a more than common Capacity, and greater Modesty and Humility, yet most equal and undaunted in Danger, Religious as well as Ingenuous, without Affection, an easie Mistress, and good Neighbour . . . neither lavish nor penurious, but an Example of Industry, as well as of other Vertues . . ."

She died near her fiftieth birthday at Hoddeson, probably at Rawdon House, in Hertfordshire on the 23d of February, 1694, and there Penn wrote to Robert Turner three days later, "My extream great affliction for ye decease of my dear wife makes me unfit to write much, whom ye Great God took to himselfe, from ye troubles of this exerciseing world . . . In great peace & sweetness she departed & so her gain but our Incomperable loss, being one of ten thousand, goode, wise, chaist, humble, plain, modest, industrious, constant & undaunted . . . but god is God, & Good & so I stop, tho afflicted not forsaken . . ."[79]

Penn's devoted friends well appreciated Guli's fortitude through many trials, the strength Penn derived from her undauntedness, and the deep grief her loss brought to this sensitive man. The day after Guli's death Henry Gouldney wrote to Sir John Rodes of Penn's irreplaceable loss,

". . . this day after long weakness, came the news of the Decease of our dear ffrd W.P.'s wife; a man of many sorrows indeed, for as he is natturally of a most affectionate temper, so, when a great object of that affection is removed, it cannot but have a deep impreshion upon so sensible (sensitive) a minde. She was a virtuous woman, had a noble regard to truth, wch wth the advantage of a temper not easily moved to extreams, she have for a long time borne up above the frightful apprehensions of the many dangers her dear husband has undergone; and although the Lord has been by an immediate hand his strength and support under them all, her constancy and undauntedness doubtless have all along added to his . . ."[80]

Gouldney expressed the hope that the Lord would send William Penn a double portion of support since half of his strength had been taken away by the death of his wife.

William I. Hull, Penn's most scholarly biographer, well evaluates the effect of Guli's loss upon her husband: "Gulielma lived long enough to rejoice with her husband over his acquittal and liberation, but died six months before the restoration of his province. The loss of his wife cast a permanent shadow over his spirit, and from this time, despite his two public triumphs of 1693 and 1694, he entered into the clouds which enclosed the later years of his life."[81]

Every known contemporary document concerning Gulielma Maria Penn has been mentioned in this modest biography. More would be conjecture. Penn, Ellwood and John Aubrey all speak of her unusual mental gifts as well as her spiritual and physical endowments. All America, as well as Pennsylvania, undoubtedly owes an incalculable debt of gratitude to this valiant and quiet lady whose sympathy and understanding strengthened Penn's ethical, philosophical and religious development, encouraged him in the formation of a government based on toleration and brotherhood, helped him plant the seed of democracy in this new land.

References and notes

1. William Penn to Gulielma Penn, Aug. 4, 1682 (1760 copy), Etting Papers, Early Quakers, 2. Historical Society of Pennsylvania (HSP).
2. William Penn to Gulielma Penn Aug. 6, 1684, Pierpont Morgan Library, New York, by whose permission this extract is quoted.
3. William Penn to Margaret Fox, Oct. 22, 1684, Thirnbeck Mss., Friends House, London.
4. All information in this text concerning the Springetts, Mary Proud and the Penington family is derived from Maria Webb, *The Penns and Peningtons of the Seventeenth Century* (London, 1867), especially "Experiences in the Life of Mary Penington," as quoted by Webb, unless otherwise noted.
5. Thomas Ellwood, *The History of the Life of Thomas Ellwood Written By Himself* (Philadelphia, n.d.), 9,10.
6. L. V. Hodgkin, *Gulielma: Wife of William Penn* (New York and London, 1947), 54–56. Hodgkin quotes the 1725 London edition of Thomas Ellwood's *Life*, which was not available to me. As this edition has an earlier flavor than later ones, I have derived all direct quotes of Ellwood from Hodgkin, but have omitted a number of Ellwood's redundant phrases, without filling the text with the customary indications of omission.
7. Mary Penington, in Hodgkin, 40.
8. Portrait of Lady Springett, #7 in auction sale catalogue, "Old Furniture, Pictures, etc. Friday May 3, 1935, Puttick & Simpson, London," Albert Cook Myers Collection, vol. 54, Chester County Historical Society, West Chester, Pa.
9. Hodgkin, 30–47.
10. Ellwood (Philadelphia, n.d.), 120–165.
11. John Vaughan to Gulielma Springett, Dec. 8, 1664. The original of this letter was in the possession of Guli's descendants, the Misses Penn-Gaskell of London, in 1914 when photographed by Albert Cook Myers. Photograph Myers Collection, vol. 54, Chester County Historical Society.
12. Oliver Lawson Dick, ed., *Aubrey's Brief Lives* (London, 1950), 235–6.

13. Ellwood (Philadelphia, n.d.), 166–179; Hodgkin, 88–91.
14. Webb, 207–214.
15. Hodgkin, 93, 94.
16. William I. Hull, *William Penn, A Topical Biography* (London, 1937), 79.
17. *Ibid.*, 33n, 109; Hodgkin, 123.
18. Sir William Penn to William Penn, October 12 and October 22, 1667, Granville Penn Book, 17, HSP.
19. Albert Cook Myers, *William Penn's Early Life in Brief* (Moylan, 1937), 60–62.
20. Hodgkin, 124.
21. Description of Penn by Sir Samuel Starling, Lord Mayor of London. Hodgkin 146n; Hull, 185.
22. George Fox, *Journal* (London, 1765), 308–404. By collating the chronology of the Fox *Journal* with the Harvey Chronicle, Ellwood's *Life* and Admiral Penn's letters of October 12 and 22, 1667, we are bound to conclude that the traditional meeting of William Penn and Gulielma Springett most likely took place late in the summer of 1668 after both had been following Quaker meeting tours which wound up in London. Admiral Penn's letter of October 22, 1667 establishes that William had not yet returned home from his Irish journey at that date. The following winter months would not be fruitful for a preaching excursion. There was apparently a period of peace in the Penn household after October 1667 and before William Penn went upon the summer tour from which reports of his activities aroused his father's ire and apprehension.
23. Harvey Mss. in Hodgkin, 124, 125.
24. Joseph Besse, *The Works of William Penn* (London, 1726), I, 3–4.
25. Hull, 112.
26. William Penn to Gulielma Springett, William Penn Letter Book 1667–1675, 103. HSP.
27. Hull, 182–184.
28. William Penn to Gulielma Springett, Dec. 1668, William Penn Letter Book 1667–1675, 43–44.
29. Thomas Ellwood in Hodgkin, 99–102.
30. "William Penn's Journal of His Second Visit to Ireland," *Pennsylvania Magazine of History and Biography, PMHB,* 40 (1916), 46–84.

31. Henry J. Cadbury, "Intercepted Correspondence of William Penn, 1670," *PMHB*, 70 (1946), 356–359; "More Penn Correspondence, Ireland, 1669–1670," *PMHB*, 73 (1949), 13–15.
32. Ellwood (Philadelphia, n.d.), 205–206.
33. Hull, 185–189.
34. Hodgkin, 142–143.
35. *Ibid.*, 144–145; Ellwood (Philadelphia, n.d.), 207–208.
36. William Penn to Gulielma Springett, 1671, William Penn Letter Book 1667–1675, 70; Hull 192–196.
37. Journal of George Fox, Aug. 12, 1671, in Hodgkin, 148.
38. Hodgkin, 220. He presented a duplicate to Isaac and Mary Penington. These books, with four others, black morocco bound, owned by Guli Penn, are at Friends House, London. Guli's four morocco books are Quaker tracts by George Fox, Edward Burroughs, Francis Howgill, etc. Two of them with chased silver clasps, are inscribed in the handwriting of Thomas Ellwood, "Ex Libris Gulielma Maria Springett." A sixth book from the young Guli's library is treasured in the rare book room of the Philadelphia Free Library. This is *A Collection of the Writings of Richard Hubberthorn*, printed in London, 1662. The author died a prisoner in Newgate "for the Truth's sake." The slender volume is elegantly bound in black Morocco with silver clasps and impressed on the spine with Guli's initials, GS. It is inscribed in Latin on the fly leaf by Guli's half brother, "Father had this as a gift from Sister Penn. Now Mother has given it to me [John Penington] in memory of them both. In the year 1681." Inside the cover is also written "The Gift off Thomas Ellwood," and the name of a later owner.
39. Myers, 53–55.
40. "William Penn's Journal: Kent and Sussex, 1672," *PMHB*, 68 (1944), 419–429.
41. Samuel M. Janney, *The Life of George Fox* (Philadelphia, 1893), 339, 340.
42. George Fox, *Journal* (London, 1765), 462.
43. Hull, 111, 112.
44. "The Household Account Book of Sarah Fell of Swarthmoor Hall (1676)" in Hodgkin, 161.
45. Dick, 235.

46. Webb (1867), 45–47.
47. Henry J. Cadbury, "Another Child to William and Gulielma Penn," *PMHB*, 74 (1950), 110–112.
48. Hodgkin, 158.
49. Haistwell Diary, June, July 1677, in Hodgkin, 161–162.
50. Hodgkin, 158.
51. George Fox, *Journal* (London, 1765), 557.
52. Hull, 216–223.
53. William Penn to Robert Turner, March 5, 1681, John Penn's Commonplace Book, 16, HSP.
54. William Penn to James Harrison, Aug. 25, 1681; William Penn to Thomas Janney, Aug. 21, 1681, Penn Papers, J. Francis Fisher's Copies, 1, HSP.
55. Hodgkin, 171; Hull, 30.
56. Guli's son-in-law, William Aubrey, claimed that her "Estate Layd ye foundation of the province." William Aubrey to James Steele, May 4, 1730, *PMHB*, 33 (1909), 369.
57. William Penn to Margaret Fox, Aug. 14, 1682, in Hodgkin, 165.
58. "Pennsylvania in the London Press," *PMHB*, 75 (1950), 153.
59. M. Atherton Leach, "Gulielma Maria Springett, First Wife of William Penn," *PMHB*, 57 (1933), 97–116. The scarf may be seen at the Historical Society of Pennsylvania.
60. In a will dated October 8, 1705 and codicil of the same date, William Penn left this gold piece to Laetitia, saying he had worn it about his neck ever since Guli's death. Granville Penn Book, 1, HSP.
61. Hodgkin, 171.
62. *Ibid.*, 172.
63. Henry J. Cadbury, "Another Child to William and Gulielma Penn," *PMHB*, 74 (1950), 110–112.
64. Gulielma Penn to Margaret Fox, Aug. 21, 1683, Myers Collection of Original Penn Manuscripts, Chester County Historical Society. This is the only original letter of Gulielma Penn known to be in America. See also Fox Mss. Journal March 19, 1683, ". . . went to Guilford . . . from thence to Wm Pens . . . on ye 22d day I had a very blessed meeting there." Excerpt quoted Albert Cook Myers Collection, vol. 64, 44; James Claypoole to William Penn, April 1, 1683, *PMHB*, 10 (1886), 271.
65. Gulielma Penn to Margaret Fox, n.d. [Spring, 1684], in Hodgkin, 183–184.

66. Gulielma Penn to Margaret Fox, Aug. 2, 1684, in Hodgkin, 181-2.
67. William Penn to Gulielma Penn, Aug. 6, 1684, with will of same date, Pierpont Morgan Library, New York.
68. William Penn to Margaret Fox, Oct. 22, 1684, in Hodgkin, 186-7.
69. William and Gulielma Maria Penn to Philadelphia Friends, Aug. 2, 1685, in Hodgkin, 219.
70. George Fox, Itinerary Journal, Oct. 24, 1685, in Hodgkin, 191.
71. *PMHB*, 74 (1950), 110.
72. Minutes of the Women's Quarterly Meeting, Sussex, March, 1687, extract in Myers Collection, vol. 67a, 21.
73. George Fox, Itinerary Journal, July 15, 1688, in Hodgkin, 191-2.
74. *Ibid.*, 192.
75. Hull, 269-273.
76. *Ibid.*, 277.
77. William Penn to friends in Philadelphia, Dec. 11, 1693, Penn Papers, Domestic & Miscellaneous Letters, 91, HSP.
78. William Penn, *An Account of the Blessed End of my Dear Wife Gulielma Maria Penn*, (n.d.), HSP.
79. William Penn to Robert Turner, Feb. 26, 1694, Granville Penn Book, 5, HSP.
80. Henry Gouldney to Sir John Rodes, Feb. 24, 1694, in Mrs. Godfrey L. Lampson, *A Quaker Post-Bag* (London, 1910), 54-56.
81. Hull, 278.

The Lost Years

an inspirational novel

by
Petra A. Bennett

The Lost Year
A Novel
By Petra A. Bennett

ISBN #189128004x

Library of Congrsss Catalog Card Number: 99-066953

© 1999 by CMJ Marian Publisher, INC.

Manufactured in the United States of America.

CMJ Marian Publisher, INC.
P.O. Box 661
Oak Lawn, Illinois 60454
www.cmjbooks.com